Addison-Wesley

Multiculturalism in Mathematics, Science, and Technology:

Readings and Activities

Addison-Wesley Publishing Company

Menlo Park, California • Reading, Massachusetts • New York
Don Mills, Ontario • Wokingham, England • Amsterdam • Bonn
Sydney • Singapore • Tokyo • Madrid • San Juan • Paris
Seoul, Korea • Milan • Mexico City • Taipei, Taiwan

Acknowledgments

Cover Photographs

Front   CL   Doug Allan/Science Photo Library/Photo Researchers
Back   CL   Robert Frerck/Woodfin Camp & Associates
           BL   Space Science and Engineering Center/University of Wisconsin, Madison
           BC   Collection of Linda Stinchfield, photo by Stephen Frisch*

* Photograph provided expressly for the publisher.

Cover Illustrations

Marlene May Howerton: Front CC, CR, BL, BC; Back CC, BR
Debbie Morse: Front CL; Back T, CR

Copyright © 1993 by Addison-Wesley Publishing Company, Inc.
Printed in the United States of America.

ISBN 0-201-29417-6

1 2 3 4 5 6 7 8 9 10 -WF- 95 94 93 92 91

Contents

Writers and Reviewers   1

An Introduction   3

Using the Wall Chart   8

Maria Agnesi   9
  The Curve of Agnesi   11
  The Curve of Agnesi: Another Approach   12
Al-Khowarizmi   13
  A Geometric Model for Solving Quadratic Equations   15
The Aztec   17
  Aztec Land Records   19
The Babylonians   21
  The Babylonian Right Triangle Theorem   23
  Estimating Square Roots by the Babylonian Method   24
Benjamin Banneker   25
  The Capital Plan   28
  Moonrise in Your City   29
Celestino Beltran   31
  Graphs to Go   33
George Washington Carver   35
  A Soapy Success Story   37
  Plant Doctor, Soil Doctor   39
The Celts   41
  The Chemistry of Butter   43
Chu Shih-Chieh   45
  Pascal's Triangle and Binomial Expansion   47
  Protein Combo Plate   48
Jewel Plummer Cobb   49
  Analyzing Cell Growth   51
  A Melanoma Experiment   52
Charles Richard Drew   53
  Keeping Blood Fresh   55
The Ancient Egyptians I   57
  The Ideal Figure   59
  Egyptian Coordinates   60
The Ancient Egyptians II   61
  Egyptian Multiplication   63
  The Very Large and the Very Small   64
The Ancient Egyptians III   65
  The Method of False Position   67
  False Position and Second-Degree Equations   68
Eratosthenes   69
  The Circumference of the Earth   71
  The Length of Africa   72
Bernardo Houssay   73
  What's on the Menu?   75

Hypatia 77
    Triangular, Square, and Polygonal Numbers 79
    A Problem with Many Solutions 80
The Incas 81
    Making a Quipu 83
Harvey Itano 85
    Patterns of Inheritance 87
    Deadly Disease or LIfe-Saving Trait? 88
Ernest Just 89
    Which Came First?—Embryology of the Sea Urchin 92
    The Cell Membrane—Master Regulator 93
Omar Khayyam 95
    A Look at Euclid's Fifth Postulate 97
Sonya Kovalevsky 99
    A Look at Symmetry 101
    Infinite Sequences 102
Lewis Howard Latimer 103
    Electric Experiences 105
Jan Matzeliger 107
    Shoe Preferences and Data Analysis 109
The Maya 111
    Addition with Maya Numerals 113
    Maya Time Cycles 114
Ynez Mexia 115
    A Plant Diversity Survey 117
The Native Americans I 119
    Circles, Cycles, and Ecosystems 121
The Native Americans II 123
    Growing Corn and Potatoes 125
The Navajo I 127
    Creating a Burntwater Design 129
The Navajo II 131
    Pine Pitch Antiseptic 133
Hideyo Noguchi 135
    Bacterial Growth 137
Srinivasa Ramanujan 139
    Circles and Pi 141
    A Geometric Method of Estimating Pi 142
Eloy Rodriguez 143
    Analyzing Herbs 145
The Sami 147
    Ski-Design Testing 149
Seki Kowa 151
    Determinants and Systems of Equations 153
    The *Yenri* Method 154
Granville T. Woods 155
    Electricity at Rest 157
    Electricity at Work 159
The Zuni 161
    Engineering Against Erosion 164

Teaching Notes 167

Answers 187

Writers

Thom Alcoze
Northern Arizona University
Flagstaff, Arizona

Claudette Bradley
University of Alaska
Fairbanks, Alaska

Julia Hernandez
Los Angeles, California

Tetsuyo Kashima
San Diego High School
San Diego, California

Iris Martinez Kane
San Francisco, California

Gerry Madrazo
Gilford County School System
Greensboro, North Carolina

Miriam Barrios-Chacon
Alameda High School
Alameda, California

Alverna Champion
Grand Valley State University
Allendale, Michigan

Martin Johnson
University of Maryland
College Park, Maryland

Alice Killackey
Zuni Unified School District
Zuni, New Mexico

Beatrice Lumpkin
Chicago, Illinois

Realista Rodriguez
Stuart High School
Falls Church, Virginia

Contributing Writer

James Enote
Pueblo of Zuni, New Mexico

Reviewer

Alsce Johnson
Detroit Public Schools
Detroit, Michigan

An Introduction

Demographics and Multiculturalism

As the twentieth century draws to a close, the demographic make-up of the United States is rapidly changing. The following statistics, from James A. Banks's *Teaching Strategies for Ethnic Studies*, illustrate the dramatic changes taking place in the U.S. population. The table shows the population increase for various ethnic groups during the 1970's.

Asian-American	141%
Mexican-American	93%
African-American	18%
European-American	6%

In many of the largest U.S. cities, ethnic "minorities" now make up the majority of the school-age population.

The National Research Council's *Everybody Counts* reports that "White males, thought of only a generation ago as the mainstay of the economy, will comprise only 15 percent of the net additions to the labor force between 1985 and 2000." The other 85 percent—women and people of color—are precisely those sectors of the population that are grossly under-represented in mathematics, the sciences, and engineering. For example, of Ph.D.'s awarded in engineering from 1984 to 1985, only 1.3% were African Americans and only 2.8% were Hispanics.

Multicultural education is an attempt to bring mathematics, science, and other disciplines into the lives of all students. It also comprises a new, global perspective on the history of these fields. Multicultural education includes the history and accomplishments of all people of all heritages. In particular, this includes people of African, Asian, Native-American, Pacific-Islander, and Hispanic backgrounds—groups that have frequently been underrepresented in the past.

Goals

Multiculturalism in Mathematics, Science, and Technology: Readings and Activities is designed to help infuse multicultural education into science and mathematics classrooms. Its goals are to:
• provide mathematics and science materials that help fulfill the vision of a global, multicultural education;
• provide role models that inspire all students to study mathematics and science;
• increase the mutual respect, pride, and understanding that come from the knowledge that all cultures have contributed to mathematics and science;
• help teachers respond to requirements in many states that mandate multicultural education;
• improve instruction by relating high school mathematics and science to real-world situations;
• provide materials that help teachers integrate mathematics and science.

The above goals were inspired in part by the vision of the National Council of Teachers of Mathematics (NCTM) as stated in its 1989 Curriculum Standards. The Standards require that "Students should have numerous and varied experiences related to the cultural, historical, and scientific evolution of mathematics so that they can appreciate the role of mathematics in the development of our contemporary society."

Science for All Americans by the American Association for the Advancement of Science (AAAS) shares a similar vision for effective learning and teaching: "It is important … for students to become aware that women and minorities have made significant contributions in spite of the barriers put in their way by society; that the roots of science, mathematics, and technology go back to the early Egyptian, Greek, Arabic, and Chinese cultures; and that scientists bring to their work the values and prejudices of the cultures in which they live."

Implementing the Vision

The use of multicultural materials in science and mathematics classrooms can provide new and exciting opportunities to implement the NCTM and AAAS standards. For example, the NCTM Standards emphasize that students should be exposed to the connections between mathematics and other disciplines. The connections between mathematics and the sciences are clearly seen in historical materials. Indeed, in early civilizations, all scientists were mathematicians and all mathematicians were scientists.

The standards stress teaching mathematics and science with an application-oriented, problem-solving approach. The multicultural approach shows students that science has developed over a period of time. Mathematics, too, was not born full-grown, as a set of definitions and axioms for students to memorize. Multicultural materials help to humanize mathematics and the sciences by showing that these fields developed as a human response to human needs.

The use of exploration with manipulatives to help students develop their intuition has also received much attention. The activities in *Multiculturalism in Mathematics, Science, and Technology* have been designed to introduce students to the type of mathematical and scientific reasoning used by the subjects of the units. Most of the activities naturally take a hands-on, exploratory approach to the material, as this is exactly how the first mathematician/scientists operated. They experimented. They went from the concrete to the abstract. Since students, too, learn by going from the concrete to the abstract, the multicultural history of science becomes more than a detour from "the real subject." The activities in this book can do more than generate respect for the science and mathematics developed by various cultures. They also provide a strategy to help all students learn.

Why Multiculturalism Now?

As the statistics at the beginning of this introduction indicate, it is in the national interest that students from all cultures be brought into mathematics and science. However, other factors contribute to the timeliness of multicultural education.

Recent scholarship has strengthened the conclusion that African peoples played a prominent role in creating the foundations of modern civilization. Likewise, the achievements of Asians,

Native Americans, Hispanics, and Pacific Islanders are only now being fully appreciated for their fundamental importance. It was only in 1980 that scholars realized that Aztec land records used place-value numerals and a zero symbol in a very accurate system of measurement.

Despite recent scholarship, misnomers and misconceptions remain a problem in clarifying the full scope of multicultural achievements. For example, the following mathematical principles are known by the names of later European mathematicians even though they were developed by earlier Asians and Africans: (1) the Pythagorean Theorem was developed in Babylonia 1000 years before Pythagoras, (2) Pascal's Triangle was created by Chinese and Persian mathematicians hundreds of years before Pascal, (3) a part of Fibonacci's book was copied line-for-line, diagram-for-diagram from a book that abu-Kamil wrote in Egypt 400 years earlier.

All of these mathematicians and scientists, European and non-European, did important work. Unfortunately, the names of many of the earlier Asians and Africans have been forgotten, in part because other people's names are attached to their work. The materials in *Multiculturalism in Mathematics, Science, and Technology* can make a good start in restoring this part of history.

Using Multiculturalism in Mathematics, Science, and Technology

The topics in this book have been selected to cover a broad multicultural spectrum, emphasizing the global nature of mathematics and science. In addition, topics have been chosen for classroom-appropriateness, student interest, and genuine academic content. No attempt was made to choose the "best" achievements or to be encyclopedic.

Teachers may have the natural impulse to look through the Table of Contents for material from specific cultures represented in his or her classroom. However, it is recommended that experiences from other cultures be selected as well to give students a truly global perspective.

Each unit begins with a reading on the achievements of the individual or culture highlighted in the unit. The reading is followed by critical-thinking questions that encourage students to reflect upon the reading and, in many cases, use their imagination to formulate answers. Readings and critical-thinking questions often bring in issues from social studies and give students a chance to improve language-arts skills.

Each unit contains one or two activities designed to give students an idea of the mathematical or scientific reasoning used by the subject of the unit. Although activities may be used independently of the readings, it is recommended that units be assigned as a whole whenever possible. However, the independence of the activities allows flexibility in choosing mathematics or science materials appropriate to the class.

Teaching notes are provided for each unit. These give specific suggestions for using the readings and activities, including additional background information and ideas for extensions or projects.

Forming Cooperative Learning Groups

The activities in *Multiculturalism in Mathematics, Science, and Technology* lend themselves to cooperative-learning groups. Students who learn by working together in groups, talking out their questions, and writing about the group experience are better able to internalize and master the concepts under discussion. In the process, the responsibility shifts from the teacher to the student for control of his or her own learning.

When establishing cooperative-learning groups, the size and make-up of the groups must first be determined. An optimum group size of three or four is usually agreed upon by most teachers. However, different configurations may work better with certain activities. In such cases, recommendations are made in the teaching notes.

Each group member should be assigned an individual responsibility. For example, one member can be responsible for recording results, ideas, and the final solution or conclusion. Another member can be responsible for handling calculations, with a third member responsible for obtaining materials, taking measurements, and collecting data. Another student might be designated as the group's spokesperson, with the responsibility of asking questions for the group and presenting the group's results. Responsibilities should be rotated periodically.

Guidelines for Cooperative Learning

Prior to using cooperative-learning groups for the first time, rules and procedures must be established, posted, and discussed. These rules and procedures should be enforced consistently. Some possible rules are suggested below.
• All students must participate.
• Each group member must be willing to help any other group member.
• Group members should show respect for one another and criticize ideas rather than people.
• Students should ask the teacher for help only if every member of the group has the same question.
• Group members should not talk with other groups.

Only a Beginning

The materials in *Multiculturalism in Mathematics, Science, and Technology* are only a beginning in an ongoing effort to help teachers integrate multiculturalism into science and mathematics classes. Some of the most valuable multicultural examples and activities can be those that the teacher writes with the help of the class. Several local projects have been very successful by encouraging students to write their own problems. Naturally, these problems reflect the daily life of the students' communities. Teachers may wish to network and share problems and activities that arise out of the real-world experiences of their own students.

There are many ways teachers can go beyond the mathematicians, scientists, and inventors discussed in this book. Every community has engineers, mathematicians, and scientists—women as well as men—who can be invited to talk to a class. Many community and professional organizations stand ready to help in this type of effort.

Bibliography

The following brief bibliography is intended as a starting place for those who would like additional information on multiculturalism and further sources of readings and activities.

Africa Counts, Claudia Zaslavsky. Lawrence Hill and Co., 1979.

Blacks in Science, Ivan Van Sertima, ed. Transaction Books, 1990.

Columbus Was Chinese: Discoveries and Inventions of the Far East, Hans Breuer. Herder and Herder, 1972.

Mexican American Biographies, Matt S. Meier. Greenwood Press, 1988.

Native American Mathematics, Michael P. Closs, ed. University of Texas, 1988.

Teaching Strategies for Ethnic Studies, James A. Banks. Allyn and Bacon, 1987.

Women in the Field, Marcia Myers Bonta. Texas A&M University Press, 1991.

Using the Wall Chart

The wall chart *A World of Mathematics, Science, and Technology* was developed to provide a large-scale, visual accompaniment to *Multiculturalism in Mathematics, Science, and Technology*. The wall chart includes many of the achievements described in *Multiculturalism in Mathematics, Science, and Technology*, as well as additional achievements from around the globe.

Since the wall chart is intended to provide only a small sample of the contributions that have come from various cultures around the world, the teacher is encouraged to use the wall chart as a starting point for further class activities. For example, the teacher may wish to have students choose a subject from the wall chart and prepare a report giving additional details on both the person or culture and the achievements in science, mathematics, or technology. Reports could follow the format of units in this book.

Students can also be provided with additional dots to place on the map. The teacher can ask students to identify one or more individuals or cultures that they would like to add to the wall chart and then have students prepare a brief summary of the subject to put up next to the map.

Maria Agnesi

Mathematician and Humanitarian

I n addition to her work as a mathematician, Italian scientist **Maria Gaetana Agnesi** (Ah NYA zi) achieved fame as a writer, a linguist, and a great humanitarian. Her essays on natural science and philosophy created a senstation in the academic world and her best-known mathematical work, *Instituzioni Analitiche* (*Analytical Institutions*), is regarded as one of the first thorough textbooks on calculus.

Born in 1718, Maria Agnesi was recognized as a genius at an early age. During social gatherings at her home, the young Agnesi presented theses on a wide range of topics, including logic, mechanics, chemistry, botany, zoology, minerology, and analytic geometry. At age nine, she gave a lengthy, persuasive speech advocating higher education for women. Although her presentations were made in Latin, Agnesi answered questions from the audience in the native language of each questioner. By age eleven, she was fluent in Latin, French, Greek, German, Hebrew, Spanish, and, of course, her native Italian.

Agnesi was by nature humble and retiring. By 1738, she no longer wished to participate in the gatherings at her home. Instead, she wanted to enter a convent and devote her life to helping the impoverished and underprivileged. Agnesi's father persuaded her to continue her studies. Abandoning all social life, she devoted herself completely to the study of mathematics.

For the next fourteen years, Agnesi concentrated on mathematics and wrote several acclaimed works. Her book *Instituzioni Analitiche* was a masterpiece of over 1000 pages. It included original discoveries ranging from elementary algebra to calculus and differential equations. Because of her writings, Agnesi's name is often associated with a bell-shaped curve, the *versiera of Agnesi*, whose equation is $x^2y = a^2(a - y)$. Due to its mathematical properties, as well as its applications in physics, this curve has intrigued mathematicians ever since Agnesi's day.

Maria Agnesi's book was described by the French Academy of Sciences as "the most complete and best-written work of its kind." Pope Benedict XIV awarded Agnesi a gold medal for her tremendous contribution to mathematics. In 1750, Maria Agnesi was appointed to the chair of mathematics and natural philosophy at the University of Bologna. However, Agnesi accepted the position only as an honorary title.

In 1751, at the peak of her mathematical career, Maria Agnesi began to withdraw from all mathematical and scientific endeavors. She cared for her ailing father until his death in 1752 and then took on the responsibility of caring for and educating her twenty younger brothers and sisters. She devoted the remainder of her life to humanitarian efforts, becoming the director of a home for the elderly in 1771.

Maria Agnesi

Questions for Critical Thinking

1. Maria Agnesi spoke many languages fluently. What were some of the advantages of being multilingual in the 18th century? What are some advantages of being multilingual today?

2. What do you think motivated nine-year-old Maria Agnesi to give a speech advocating higher education for women?

3. A well-known curve is named after Maria Agnesi. Give some other examples of mathematical terms or objects that bear the name of a mathematician.

4. Maria Agnesi devoted much of her life to mathematics and much of her life to social work. What do you think was her greatest achievement? Why?

Name _____   Date _____

Maria Agnesi

The Curve of Agnesi

Materials: pencil, graph paper

The curve given by the equation $x^2y = a^2(a - y)$ is called the *versiera of Agnesi*. Because of a mistaken translation from Italian, it is also known by the unusual English name, *the witch of Agnesi*. In the equation, a is a constant.

1. Write the equation for $a = 2$.

_____

2. Solve the equation for y.

_____

3. Complete the table of values below. Then plot the curve on the grid provided.

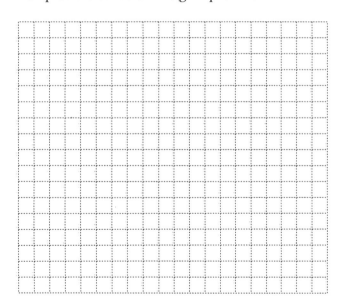

x	y
-3	
-2	
-1	
0	
1	
2	
3	

4. Describe the curve you have drawn.

_____

_____

5. How would the curve differ if $a = 5$? Rewrite the equation, create a table of values, and plot the curve on a separate piece of graph paper. Describe your results below.

_____

_____

Maria Agnesi

The Curve of Agnesi: Another Approach

Materials: pencil, graph paper, compass, straightedge

In this activity, you will graph the curve of Agnesi according to her famous definition.

1. Set up a coordinate system on a sheet of graph paper. Use a compass to draw a circle with center $(0, \frac{1}{2})$ and diameter 1.

2. Draw the horizontal line $y = 1$ on the same set of axes.

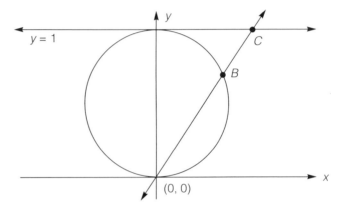

3. Using a straightedge, draw a line that passes through the origin, $(0, 0)$, and any point B on the circle. Be sure the line extends through the line $y = 1$ as shown at the right. Label the intersection of the two lines point C.

4. Draw a horizontal line through point B and a vertical line through point C. The intersection of these lines should be labeled point A. Point A is on the curve of Agnesi.

5. Find additional points on the curve by repeating the above process with different choices for point B. Be sure to select points from various parts of the circumference of the circle.

6. Sketch the curve of Agnesi by drawing a smooth curve through the points labeled A. Describe the curve.

_____

_____

_____

7. The general equation for Maria Agnesi's curve is $x^2 y = a^2(a - y)$. What value of a is used in the curve you drew? How do you know?

_____

_____

_____

_____

Al-Khowarizmi

The Origin of "Algebra"

he words *algebra, algorithm, alcohol, chemistry,* and *nadir,* all have something in common. They are technical words derived from Arabic, the leading language of science in the Middle Ages. Islamic scientists of this period came from many regions of the world and many ethnic backgrounds, but they all wrote in Arabic. One of the most famous of these was **Mohammed ibn Musa al-Khowarizmi.**

Born in what is present-day Iran, al-Khowarizmi (al koo WA riz mee) became a professor at the Arab University in Baghdad around the year 825. The Arabic name for this university was "House of Wisdom" and it was true to its name as a center of research and higher education. Subjects of study included astronomy, medicine, physics, chemistry, music, and mathematics. The illustration at the right shows architecture typical of the region in which the Arab University was located.

Around the time he was at the university, al-Khowarizmi wrote an algebra book that became famous throughout the world. Indeed, its title gave the word *algebra* to the English language. The Arabic title of this book was *Al-jabr w'al muqabalah.* The spelling of *al-jabr* eventually changed to *algebra.* In a similar way, al-Khowarizmi's own name later took on the meaning of "a mathematical procedure," and the spelling changed to the modern *algorithm.*

The *al-jabr* book showed how to solve equations, often with the use of geometric models. It described the manipulation of terms, the balancing of equations, and the use of the quadratic formula. It is interesting to note that only the positive solutions to equations were considered. Although Islamic mathematicians knew the rules for signed numbers, they ignored negative solutions since they felt such numbers had no geometric meaning. In fact, al-Khowarizmi said that the purpose of his *al-jabr* was practical and that it might be helpful in legal disputes or in measuring land.

In his writings, al-Khowarizmi also taught the use of Hindu-Arabic numerals. These were essentially the numerals 1, 2, 3, and so on, that are used today. As translations of his work reached Europe, the use of Hindu-Arabic numerals spread. Before al-Khowarizmi, Europeans had used Roman numerals that were much less convenient. Anyone who has tried to multiply MCMXCII by CCCLIV will appreciate the advantage of modern, Hindu-Arabic numerals!

Al-Khowarizmi

Questions for Critical Thinking

1. Can you think of words of Arabic origin, other than those on the previous page, that are used today in the sciences? (Hint: Many words beginning with "al" are of Arabic origin.)

_____

_____

_____

2. Al-Khowarizmi's name was eventually transformed into the word *algorithm*. Give an example of another scientist or mathematician whose name has become a common word.

_____

_____

3. Al-Khowarizmi disregarded negative solutions to equations because they did not have a geometric meaning. Are there practical uses for negative solutions? If so, give some examples.

_____

_____

_____

4. Give some examples of practical uses that *al-jabr* might have had in al-Khowarizmi's day.

_____

_____

_____

5. Give at least two advantages of modern, Hindu-Arabic numerals over Roman numerals.

_____

_____

_____

Al-Khowarizmi

A Geometric Model for Solving Quadratic Equations

Materials: pencil, algebra tiles (or paper, ruler, and scissors)

Al-Khowarizmi used geometric models to demonstrate his algebraic methods of solving quadratic equations. Consider the following problem.

A square is extended in one direction by 8 feet. The resulting rectangle has an area of 33 square feet. What is the length of each side of the original square?

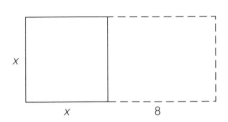

To set up an equation, let x be the length of each side of the original square. Then the original square has an area of x^2 feet. The extension is 8 feet long in one direction and x feet long in the other, so its area is $8x$. Adding these areas together and setting them equal to 33 gives the equation $x^2 + 8x = 33$.

Two methods of solving this equation are presented below. The first is a purely algebraic method. The second is al-Khowarizmi's geometric method.

Completing the Square

1. The left side of the equation, $x^2 + 8x$, is not a perfect square. What integer must be added to this to form a perfect square?

    _____

2. Add this integer to both sides of the equation.

    $x^2 + 8x +$ _____ $= 33 +$ _____

3. Write the left side of the equation as a perfect square.

    (_____$)^2 =$ _____

4. The expression in parentheses must be equal to the positive or negative square root of the number on the right. Use this to write two equations.

    _____

5. Solve the equations for x.

    $x =$ _____ or _____

6. What is the length of each side of the original square? (Remember to disregard negative values of x since lengths are always positive.)

    _____

Al-Khowarizmi

A Geometric Model *(continued)*

Al-Khowarizmi's Geometric Model

1. To solve the problem, Al-Khowarizmi's geometric model begins with a square of unknown area, x^2. This can be represented with one large square algebra tile. If you do not have algebra tiles, cut a square from a piece of paper.

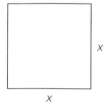

2. Extend the square in one direction by adding 8 rectangles, each with dimensions 1 by x. Arrange 8 rectangular algebra tiles as shown. If you do not have algebra tiles, cut the rectangles from a piece of paper.

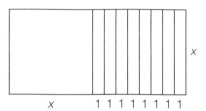
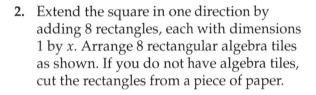

3. Rearrange the 8 rectangles as shown.

4. To make a large square, as shown at the far right, smaller squares must be added to the corners. Use small square algebra tiles or small squares cut from a piece of paper to do this.

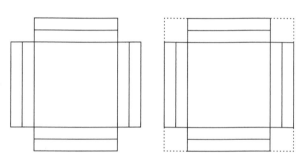

   What is the area of each corner?

   _____

   What is the total area of the four corners?

   _____

5. The area of the large square is 33 plus the areas of the four corners. What is the area of the large square?

   _____

6. Take the square root of your result in Step 5 to find the length of each side of the large square.

   _____

7. Subtract the lengths of the sides of the corner squares to find the length of each side of the original square.

   _____

The Aztec

Markets, Maize, and Mathematics

When Spanish troops first saw the Aztec capital of Tenochtitlan in 1519, they could not believe their eyes. The beautiful city was built on an island in the middle of Lake Texcoco and was linked to the mountainous mainland by raised roads. To the soldiers, the towers, temples, and lakes in Tenochtitlan must have seemed like something from a dream. As shown in the illustration at the right, the Aztec temples were built in the form of pyramids.

The city of Tenochtitlan, which was on the site of present-day Mexico City, was larger than any in Spain. Its markets were visited by 50,000 customers each day. The markets' stores were bulging with the rich products of the advanced Aztec civilization. A court of judges remained in session at the markets to peacefully settle disputes that arose between buyers and sellers.

To help keep accurate accounts for their extensive commerce, the Aztec had developed an efficient system of numerals and arithmetic. Aztec numerals were of two types. For commercial uses, the numerals were made up of dots, vertical strokes, and a zero symbol. For other occasions, more decorative numerals were used. Although the concepts of place value and a number base of 20 had been borrowed from the earlier Maya and Olmec Native Americans, the numerals were distinctly Aztec. For example, a small ear of corn was used for the zero symbol. Corn, or maize, was the material base of most Central American civilizations. Its use as the zero symbol shows how important the concept was to the Aztec.

Among the applications of Aztec mathematics, the records that registered land ownership were of special importance. Land records gave the boundaries, the area, and the market value of property. The Aztec government used these records to calculate the amount of tax that the owners had to pay.

Recently, comparisons were made between the Aztec land records and records of the same farms that were drawn up by the Spanish conquerors. Although Spain was a leader in European science and mathematics, the Aztec records were more accurate. This may be because the Aztec unit of area, the square *quahuitl*, was reliable and did not change from farm to farm. The *caballeria*, the Spanish unit of area, varied considerably, perhaps for political purposes. In addition, perhaps the Aztec had more practice in planning cities and building pyramids that required accurate measurements.

The Aztec

Questions for Critical Thinking

1. What types of calculations might have been needed in a market attended by 50,000 people?

    _____

    _____

    _____

    _____

2. The Aztec had two types of numerals—one for commerce and one for other uses. Why do you think this was the case?

    _____

    _____

    _____

    _____

3. How might a changeable unit of measure, such as the Spanish *caballeria,* be used for political purposes?

    _____

    _____

    _____

    _____

4. Why would the Aztec have needed accurate measurements in building their pyramids?

    _____

    _____

    _____

    _____

Name _____   Date _____

Aztec Land Records

Materials: pencil, graph paper, ruler, compass, calculator

Agriculture was an important part of the Aztec civilization. Farmers grew many crops, including corn, squash, and tomatoes. In order to keep track of the farms, the Aztec kept land records that included information on the area of each farm.

The records show that farms were seldom rectangular because the terrain was rough. Despite this, the calculations were quite accurate. How did the Aztec calculate the areas of their farms? Although this is not completely known, the following facts have been discovered.

- Accurate measuring ropes were available. The ropes measured length with a unit called a *quahuitl* (about 2.5 meters). For greater accuracy, fractions of a *quahuitl* could be used.

- The basic unit of area was the square *quahuitl*.

- Lengths of the sides of a field were measured and recorded. Small sketches may have been made, as shown on the following page.

1. The figures on the following page show the dimensions of six farms measured in *quahuitls*. For each farm, make a scale drawing on graph paper using one square of the graph paper to represent one square *quahuitl*. In some cases, you will need to use a compass to locate the intersection of sides. An example is shown below.

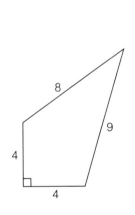
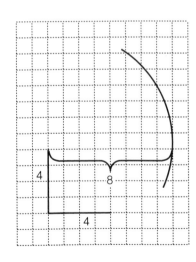
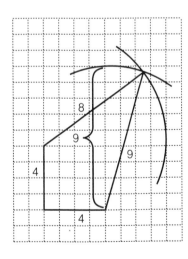

2. Estimate the area of each farm by counting the number of graph-paper squares in each scale drawing. Record your estimates in the spaces provided.

3. Find the area of each farm using a calculator and the formulas below. Farms that are not rectangular or triangular should first be divided up into these figures. Record your answers in the spaces provided.

Area of rectangle = length × width
Area of triangle = $\frac{1}{2}$ base × height

The Aztec

Aztec Land Records *(continued)*

1.

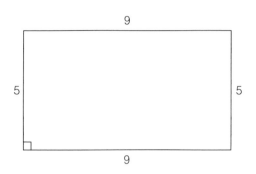

Estimate _____

Area _____

2.

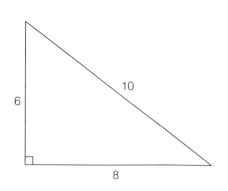

Estimate _____

Area _____

3.

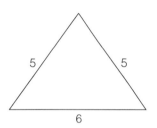

Estimate _____

Area _____

4.

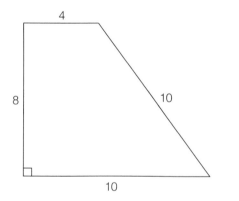

Estimate _____

Area _____

5.

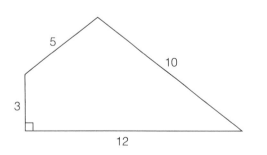

Estimate _____

Area _____

6.

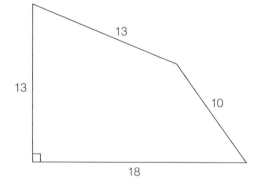

Estimate _____

Area _____

The Babylonians

The Pythagorean Theorem Before Pythagoras

I f you had been a student in ancient Babylonia, your "notebooks" would have been made of clay. Instead of a pencil, you would have used a pointed tool, called a stylus, to press symbols into the soft clay. After the teacher checked your work, you could have wiped the soft clay clean to start a new lesson. Once the tablets were baked they could last indefinitely in the desert climate. Although the clay tablets were very heavy, they were also very permanent.

As these tablets are found and translated, modern scientists are learning a lot about the people of Babylonia. Located in present-day Iraq, Babylonia was bounded by the Tigris and Euphrates Rivers. So far, the tablets that scientists have discovered in this region may number in the millions. Some of these tablets have given us an idea of the topics the Babylonians studied.

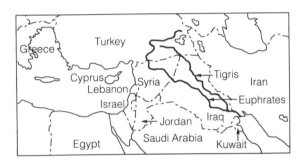

As a student in ancient Babylonia, you would have studied mathematics and many of the same subjects that are studied today. One of your math topics would have been the right triangle theorem, known today as the Pythagorean Theorem. Naturally, you would not have called the theorem "Pythagorean" in ancient Babylonia since Pythagoras would not be born for another one-thousand years.

In order to use the right triangle theorem, you would have first learned to do quick calculations with the efficient Babylonian numerals. It was a place-value system based on the number sixty. Although our current system is based on the number ten, a base-sixty system is still used to measure time and angles. For example, we still have sixty minutes in one hour and sixty minutes in one degree.

Unfortunately, students did not leave any tablets with notes about the right triangle theorem. (At least none have been found yet.) However, a tablet was found that tells part of the story. This tablet, called Plimpton 322, of the Columbia University collection, was dug up intact in modern times. Then, having survived more than 4000 years buried in the sand of Iraq, someone dropped the tablet and a piece broke off. Nobody knows where the broken part is. Nonetheless, the remaining portion of the tablet lists numbers that are very likely related to the right triangle theorem. The tablet is illustrated at the right.

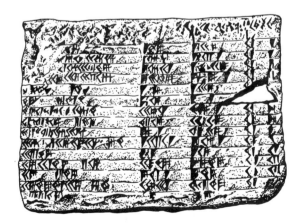

The Babylonians

Questions for Critical Thinking

1. Why do you think the Babylonians made their records on clay?

    _____

    _____

    _____

2. What evidence do you have that the Babylonian civilization was fairly wealthy?

    _____

    _____

    _____

3. Why is the right triangle theorem so important?

    _____

    _____

    _____

4. The Babylonian number system was based on the number 60. Why was 60 a more convenient choice than other numbers, such as 59 or 61?

    _____

    _____

    _____

5. What other information about life in ancient Babylonia might scientists be able to learn from tablets?

    _____

    _____

    _____

    _____

The Babylonians

The Babylonian Right Triangle Theorem

Materials: pencil, calculator

The columns of numbers on the Babylonian tablet known as Plimpton 322 are related to the right triangle theorem. Translated into modern, base-ten numbers, they can be used to generate the numbers shown in the table below.

	119	169
	3367	4825
	4601	6649
	65	97
	319	481
	2291	3541
	799	1249
	481	769
	4961	8161
	45	75

1. Compare the two columns of numbers. Are any patterns immediately apparent?

   _____

2. Use your calculator to experiment with the numbers in the first row. Can the numbers 119 and 169 be used as two of the three numbers in the right triangle theorem? That is, is there any way you can fit them into $c^2 = a^2 + b^2$ or $b^2 = c^2 - a^2$?.

   _____

3. What number did you use with 119 and 169 to fit them into the right triangle theorem? Place the number in the left column of the first row.

4. Use a similar method to complete the rest of the table.

5. Describe the relationship among the numbers in your completed table.

   _____

The Babylonians

Estimating Square Roots by the Babylonian Method

The ancient Babylonians had a fairly simple method for estimating square roots. For example, to estimate $\sqrt{17}$, the Babylonians would have used the following steps.

a. Make an "educated guess" at a whole number close to $\sqrt{17}$. The whole number 4 is a good guess, since $4^2 = 16$.

b. Divide 17 by 4. (This can simply be written as $\frac{17}{4}$.)

c. Take the average of 4 and $\frac{17}{4}$.

$$\frac{1}{2}(4 + \frac{17}{4}) = \frac{1}{2}(\frac{33}{4}) = \frac{33}{8} = 4\frac{1}{8} \text{ or } 4.125$$

The result, 4.125, should be a reasonable estimate of $\sqrt{17}$.

d. Check. Is $(4.125)^2$ close to 17? Although the Babylonians would have had to square 4.125 by hand, you can use a calculator to see that $(4.125)^2$ is approximately 17.2.

If greater accuracy is desired, the process can be continued by dividing 17 by 4.125 and then averaging this number with 4.125.

Why does the method work? Notice that $4(\frac{17}{4}) = 17$. Since 4 is too small to be the square root of 17, $\frac{17}{4}$ must be too large. Therefore, it makes sense to average these values to obtain a better estimate.

1. Use the Babylonian method to find $\sqrt{15}$.

   a. Guess a whole number close to $\sqrt{15}$. _____

   b. Divide 15 by this number. _____

   c. Average your answers to 1a and 1b to get an estimate for $\sqrt{15}$. _____

   d. Check by squaring. _____

2. Use the square root key on your calculator to find $\sqrt{15}$. _____

3. How does your estimate in Question 1c compare to the value of $\sqrt{15}$ given by your calculator?

4. Does it matter what whole number you choose to begin the process in Question 1a? Try a different guess and complete the process. Do you get a more accurate or less accurate estimate for $\sqrt{15}$?

Benjamin Banneker

From Stars to City Planning

uring the early years of United States history, Benjamin Banneker made a name for himself as a self-taught mathematician and astronomer. Banneker is most famous for his contributions to the planning of Washington, D.C., in 1790–1791. As the astronomer for the six-person surveying team, Banneker helped determine the outline for the city. When the head of the planning committee abruptly resigned, taking the plans with him, it is said that Banneker reproduced the entire city plan from memory. A section of the plan is illustrated at the right.

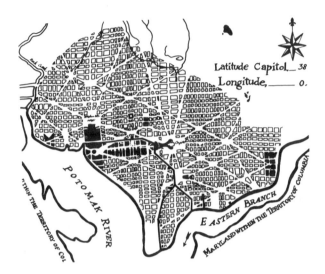

Almanacs of astronomical tables published by Banneker represent his greatest scientific achievement. Using borrowed astronomy books and instruments, Banneker taught himself how to calculate the positions of the planets and how to predict the dates of lunar and solar eclipses. His first unpublished astronomical tables were completed in 1791. Thousands of calculations were required to create these data tables, which gave the rising times, setting times, and sky locations for the sun, moon, and planets on each day of the year. Some of the tables were based on Banneker's direct observations. Others were the result of Banneker's calculations. In the 1790's, time zones were not standardized and each city had its own local time. Banneker performed calculations that adapted existing nautical almanac tables for local latitude, longitude, and time.

Banneker continued to calculate data and publish almanacs from 1792 to 1804. Banneker sent a copy of his first published almanac to Secretary of State Thomas Jefferson. Jefferson was impressed with Banneker's work and sent the manuscript to the French Academy of Sciences. The almanacs were distributed internationally by the anti-slavery movement and Banneker's achievements were described as "proof that the powers of the mind are disconnected with the colour of the skin." The title page of the 1795 almanac is shown at the right.

Benjamin Banneker

From Stars to City Planning *(continued)*

Banneker was already 60 years old when he published his almanacs, but his gift for science and mathematics showed itself much earlier. As a child, Banneker created his own mathematical puzzles. He was taught to read and write by his grandmother, an indentured servant who bought her freedom and that of Banneker's African grandfather, Banaka. Benjamin grew up on his parents' farm and attended a country school for a short time. Each day, when the farm work was done, he used his reading and writing skills to educate himself in literature, history, and mathematics. At age 22, he amazed his neighbors by building a striking clock with only a borrowed pocket watch as a model. He calculated the proper ratios of the gears and wheels, and carved the parts by hand from seasoned wood.

Banneker was 50 years old when he began studying astronomy and surveying. The Ellicotts, a family of surveyors and mill owners, had moved nearby. Banneker befriended George Ellicott, an enthusiastic amateur astronomer. Ellicott gladly loaned books and instruments to Banneker. In a few months, Banneker had mastered the use of logarithms and was making astronomical computations. On a visit to the area, surveyor Andrew Ellicott saw Banneker's work and arranged for him to become part of the surveying team for the new capital city, Washington, D.C. The result of Banneker's surveying and astronomical work can be seen in the monumental capital city known today.

Questions for Critical Thinking

1. Today, nine planets are known to revolve around the sun. In 1790, only seven, including Earth, were known. Why do you think only seven planets had been discovered by 1790?

   _____

   _____

   _____

2. In 1790, what were the seven known planets?

   _____

   _____

3. Banneker taught himself astronomy by reading, observation, and trial-and-error calculation. Describe some steps you could take to learn more about a subject if no schools or teachers were available.

   _____

   _____

Benjamin Banneker

Questions for Critical Thinking *(continued)*

4. In the 1790's, every city had its own local time. Would such a system work today? Why or why not?

_____

_____

_____

_____

5. Why might an astronomical table with the rising and setting times of the sun, moon and planets have been useful to people in 1790? Would such a table be useful to people today? Explain your answer.

_____

_____

_____

_____

6. Why is it necessary to survey the land before building a city? What might a city be like if this is not done?

_____

_____

_____

_____

7. What mathematics might Banneker have needed to build his clock?

_____

_____

_____

_____

Benjamin Banneker

The Capital Plan: Relative Error and Percent Error

Materials: pencil, calculator

The accuracy of the city plan for Washington, D.C., depended on the work of Benjamin Banneker, astronomer for the surveying team. Because the Earth's surface is curved, accurate measurement of such a large area (100 square miles) required the use of certain stars as reference points. How close did the team get to their goal of marking out a square ten miles long on each side? The actual measurements are shown in the figure.

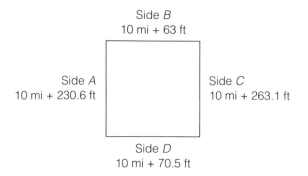

Notice that every side of the "square" is a slightly different length. This is due to measurement errors. Are these errors significant? For example, Side C is 263.1 feet too long. Is 263.1 feet a large error? That depends on the size of the measurement being made. The distance 263.1 feet (nearly the length of one football field) would be a very large error if the measurements were for the construction of your school. But is it a large error compared to the 10-mile boundary for an entire city?

The way to answer this question is to compare the size of the error to the correct value of the desired measurement. This is done by calculating the **relative error.** As shown below, relative error is found by dividing the size of the error by the size of the desired measurement. This quantity can be converted to **percent error** if you multiply it by one hundred.

Relative error = Error ÷ Desired length
Percent error = Relative error × 100

1. Find the error, relative error, and percent error of the Washington, D.C., 10-mile square measurements. (Hint: Keep in mind that 1 mile equals 5280 feet.)

	Error	Relative Error	Percent Error
Side A			
Side B			
Side C			
Side D			

2. Does the percent error for each of the four sides seem small or large? Explain.

_____

_____

Benjamin Banneker   **29**

Moonrise in Your City

Materials: pencil, calculator, globe (optional)

What time does the moon rise in
your city? The time of moonrise
depends on several factors: your
city's location on the globe, the day
of the year, and your time zone.
Every 24 hours, the earth makes one
rotation on its axis, moving in an
easterly direction. One complete
rotation measures 360 degrees. Each
degree is known as a degree of
longitude. For historical reasons,
the site of a major observatory at
Greenwich, England was chosen as
zero longitude. Degrees of longitude
are measured to the east and west of
an imaginary curve passing through
Greenwich and the earth's poles.

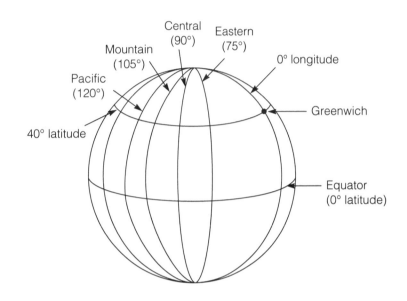

To measure north-south distances, degrees of **latitude** are used. The equator is defined as
zero latitude. Lines of latitude and longitude together form a giant grid that can be used to
pinpoint any location on Earth. If a globe is available, find your city and locate the nearest
lines of longitude and latitude.

Given that the time of moonrise is 6:03 P.M. in Greenwich, England (0° longitude and 40°
latitude) on December 22, 1991, you can calculate the time of moonrise on that day for the
cities in the table on the following page. To simplify calculations, assume that the latitude
for all of these cities is 40°. To calculate the time of moonrise, you will need to make two
different corrections.

- To correct for longitude, you need to know that on December 23, 1991 (one day later), as
  the earth turned 360°, moonrise in Greenwich advanced to 7:21 P.M. That is, the moon
  rose 78 minutes later after the earth moved though 360° of longitude. For each of the
  cities listed in the table, a fraction of that 78 minutes must be added to Greenwich
  moonrise time of 6:03 P.M. The number of minutes to be added depends on the fraction
  each city's longitude is of the total 360° rotation of the earth. Thus, the following formula
  is useful.

$$\text{Correction for longitude} = \frac{\text{longitude}}{360°} \times 78 \text{ minutes}$$

- To correct for position in a time zone, add 4 minutes of time for each degree of longitude
  past the start of the time zone. To understand why the moon will rise later at the west
  end of a time zone than the east end, you need to know that each 1-hour time zone
  covers 15° of longitude. Therefore, 4 minutes correspond to 1 degree of longitude.

Multiculturalism in Mathematics, Science, and Technology   **29**

Benjamin Banneker

Moonrise in Your City (continued)

Fill in the table below using the following steps. The calculations for Indianapolis are shown as an example.

1. Convert degree-minute longitude measure to decimal degrees, rounded to two decimal places. To do this, divide the number of minutes in the longitude by 60, and add the decimal amount to the number of degrees. For example, the longitude in Indianapolis, in degrees and minutes, is 86° 10′. The calculation is shown below.

$$10 \div 60 = 0.17$$

$$0.17° + 86° = 86.17°$$

2. Divide the longitude by 360° and multiply the result by 78 minutes of time. For Indianapolis, this is 86.17° divided by 360° or 0.239. Multiply 0.239 by 78 to get 19 minutes of time for the longitude correction.

3. Add 4 minutes of time for each degree of longitude past the beginning of the time zone. For example, Indianapolis is at 86.17° and the Eastern time zone begins at 75°. This is a difference of 11.17°. Multiply 11.17 by 4 minutes to get 44.68, which may be rounded off to 45 minutes.

4. Add the corrections from Steps 2 and 3 and add this total to 6:03 P.M. For Indianapolis, the corrections from Steps 2 and 3 total 64 minutes. Adding 64 minutes to 6:03 P.M. gives 7:07 P.M. for moonrise in Indianapolis on December 22, 1991.

City	Longitude (deg/min)	Longitude (decimal)	Longitude Divided by 360°	Longitude Time Correction	Local Time Correction	Moonrise 12/22/91
Philadelphia	75° 9′					
Columbus	83°					
Indianapolis	86° 10′	86.17°	0.239	19 min.	45 min.	7:07 P.M.
Denver	104° 59′					
Sacramento	121° 30′					

5. Suppose you want to calculate the time of moonrise on December 22, 1991, in your city. What factors do you need to take into account to modify the above calculations?

_____

_____

Celestino Beltran

Software Savvy

Celestino Beltran, a Mexican-American engineer, is President and Chief Executive of Comprehensive Technologies International (CTI), a technology and software-development company. *Software* is a program of detailed instructions that tells a computer how to perform a task. Today, software companies are on the cutting edge of science, technology, and the business world as they develop products that change the way work is done. For example, software developed by CTI could reduce health-care costs by streamlining the way doctor bills and hospital bills are processed.

When you watch a computer in action, it may seem to have a mind of its own. But this is not the case. A computer can only work with information in ways determined by the instructions it is given. Software development engineers, such as Celestino Beltran, must be able to analyze how a task is performed and write detailed, step-by-step instructions for the computer to follow. One way of organizing this information is in a *flow chart*.

A flow chart is like a map of the steps needed to complete a task. Each box in a flow chart contains one instruction. Because some instructions involve making choices, there can be several arrows leading from a box. Each arrow leads to a box describing the next instruction appropriate to that choice. The figure at the right illustrates a flow chart for the simple task of washing your hair.

Flow charts are useful tools for organizing even the most complicated tasks. They make it easy to see what is happening at any step in the process. Other powerful tools for organizing information include matrices, graphs, charts, and models.

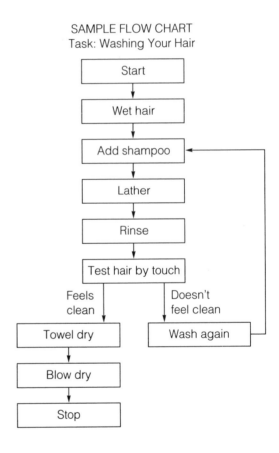

SAMPLE FLOW CHART
Task: Washing Your Hair

Celestino Beltran credits his engineering courses for his ability to clearly organize information. However, he points out that it was a long and difficult road to engineering school and his professional success. Until age 14, Beltran was illiterate. He had been dismissed as uneducable by his teachers at the public high school in El Monte—a town 20 km east of Los Angeles. However, his parents, who had little formal education, insisted that he finish high school. A summer remedial reading class changed Beltran's life. He learned to read and became excited about learning. After graduating from a private high school, he decided to become an engineer, an occupation he discovered while working as a ditch digger on a construction crew.

Celestino Beltran

Software Savvy *(continued)*

At first, Beltran was rejected by every engineering school to which he applied because of his low score on the Scholastic Aptitude Test. Fortunately, one engineering school, Loyola Marymount, suggested that he take a pre-engineering program at a community college. After three years at the community college, Beltran entered Loyola Marymount as a junior. He graduated with a degree in Civil Engineering two years later.

After college, Beltran served in the military. He then returned from active duty with the U.S. Army Corp of Engineers and worked in East Los Angeles on several economic development programs over the next eight years. Beltran moved to the Washington, D.C., area in 1980 to found CTI. CTI now employs over five hundred people and produces more than thirty-three million dollars in yearly revenues. Today, Celestino Beltran and CTI's vice-president, Alfred Navarro, recommend computer technology to students as a great "equalizer" that can change the face of the working world and open doors for anyone willing to learn.

Questions for Critical Thinking

1. Why do you think even the most sophisticated computer does not have "a mind of its own"?

_____

_____

_____

2. Celestino Beltran and Alfred Navarro consider computer technology a great "equalizer." Explain in your own words what they might mean by this.

_____

_____

_____

3. Study the sample flow chart on the previous page. In the space at the right, design a flow chart for a familiar task. You may wish to use an everyday activity, a hobby, or a work-related task.

Name _____ Date _____

Graphs to Go

Materials: pencil, graph paper, straightedge, colored pens, almanac or other reference book

Graphs are very helpful in communicating data or information. Although Celestino Beltran uses a computer to prepare his graphs and charts, he learned how to construct graphs using paper and pencil. In this activity, you will construct two basic types of graphs: a **line graph** and a **bar graph.** These graphs, as well as other types of graphs, make information compact and "ready to go."

Line graphs and bar graphs have two axes: the horizontal *x*-axis and the vertical *y*-axis. These are shown at the right. The *x*-axis is used to plot the *independent variable*. In many graphs, the independent variable is time. The graph then expresses how data changes over a period of time. Often, the *y*-axis is used to plot data for what is called the *dependent variable*. A dependent variable is usually a variable you wish to study, or in the case of an experiment, the variable you deliberately change. In the following activity, you will collect data that can be represented in a line or bar graph.

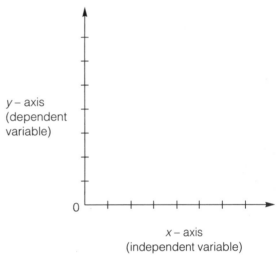

1. Use an almanac or other reference book to collect some type of data for each month of the year. For example, you may wish to look up the average rainfall in your town for each month. Record the data in the table below.

Month	Data	Month	Data
January		July	
February		August	
March		September	
April		October	
May		November	
June		December	

2. Draw a horizontal *x*-axis and a vertical *y*-axis on the top half of your graph paper. Label the *x*-axis with the unit of time (months) and the *y*-axis with the appropriate unit (inches, for example, if your data is for rainfall).

Celestino Beltran

Graphs to Go *(continued)*

3. Examine the data in your table. What are the highest and lowest values?

   _____

4. Determine the scale for each axis using the highest-to-lowest range. Make sure that the spacing is uniform. For example, you may wish to have four squares of the graph paper between each month on the *x*-axis. Label the axes.

5. Plot each data point by first locating the month on the *x*-axis and the data value on the *y*-axis. Place a dot where the lines through these values meet. Do this for all twelve months. When you have located all of the points, connect them with line segments. You have now completed the line graph. Give the line graph a title describing the data it contains. Write the title on your graph and in the space below.

   _____

6. Make a bar graph for the data in your table as follows. Prepare a set of axes, as you did in Step 4, on the bottom half of the graph paper. Assign one vertical column (stack) of grid squares to each month on the *x*-axis.

7. Plot the data by shading or coloring in an appropriate stack of grid squares for each month. When you have finished, give the bar graph a title.

8. Compare the line graph and the bar graph that you have constructed. How are they similar?

   _____

   _____

   _____

9. How are the graphs different?

   _____

   _____

   _____

Extension

Many software programs can create graphs from numerical data. Research the various graphing programs that are available and find one that you think would be appropriate for creating the graphs in this activity.

George Washington Carver

Products from Peanuts

I n the early 1900's, African-American botanist **George Washington Carver** (ca. 1860–1943) won international fame for agricultural research. He was a pioneer in the science of chemurgy, the chemistry of raw materials derived from farm products. He developed a wide variety of useful products from crops such as peanuts (illustrated at the right), sweet potatoes, and pecans. Carver's work helped convince cotton farmers in the South that growing a variety of crops would provide them with new sources of income.

To provide an economic incentive for growing a variety of crops, Carver went to his laboratory and developed new commercial uses for them. In an astounding feat of chemistry, Carver made more than 300 products from the peanut. The products ranged from instant coffee to soaps, inks, and cosmetics. He developed 118 different products from the sweet potato, including flour, candy, mucilage, and synthetic rubber. Carver was able to produce 75 products from the pecan, a tree native to the South. He made synthetic marble from wood shavings, and paint pigments from local clays. Leftover cotton stalks were turned into starch, gum, and wallboard. When the supply of imported synthetic dyes was cut off during World War I, Carver was able to prepare 500 different dyes using only 28 plant species.

In addition to his laboratory work, Carver saw to it that scientific agricultural methods were made available to rural farmers. Carver had a sophisticated understanding of soil ecology and conservation. He recognized that many years of growing only cotton had worn out the soil on farms throughout the South. To help restore the soil, Carver developed and taught methods of crop rotation. He recommended that legumes, such as peanuts, clover, and soybeans, be planted every few years to add nitrogen to the soil. He also made a soil-enriching fertilizer from plant materials, such as leaves and stalks, which had previously been burned or thrown away.

Even as a child in the 1860's, Carver was interested in local plants and rocks. He grew up on a Missouri plantation where his parents were slaves and became known as the "plant doctor" as he learned the names of plants and their growth habits. Carver later wrote of his childhood, "I had an inordinate desire for knowledge... I wanted to know every strange stone, flower, insect, bird, or beast." He left home in his teens to work and attend school in various small towns in the Midwest. Carver earned his way through college by cooking, operating a laundry, and working as a janitor. He graduated from Iowa State College in 1894 and was appointed assistant botanist at the agricultural experiment station. There, he concentrated on collecting fungi, particularly those known to be plant parasites. He discovered several new species which were named for him, and his collection grew to about 20,000 species, bringing him worldwide fame.

Multiculturalism in Mathematics, Science, and Technology

George Washington Carver

Products from Peanuts *(continued)*

In 1896, Carver joined the staff at Tuskegee Institute in Alabama at the invitation of Booker T. Washington. Working from scratch, Carver and his students built the first agricultural laboratory there from found materials. From these modest beginnings, Carver made discoveries and developed techniques at Tuskegee that were later adopted by rural farmers in places as far away as China, India, Zimbabwe (then called Rhodesia), and Albania.

In 1916, Carver was inducted into the Royal Society of Arts in London, an honor that few United States citizens receive. Carver was awarded the Springarn medal in 1923 for distinguished service in agricultural chemistry. Before his death in 1943, Carver used his life savings to set up a research foundation so his work could continue. The George Washington Carver Research Foundation is now a modern research organization with over one hundred faculty and staff investigators involved in pure research, training, and outreach projects.

Questions for Critical Thinking

1. Give some possible reasons why Carver may have chosen peanuts, pecans, and sweet potatoes for his research.

   _____

   _____

2. Why do you think so many different products can be made from one plant?

   _____

   _____

3. Explain how the planting of one crop, year after year, can wear out the soil.

   _____

   _____

4. Why might the agricultural techniques developed by Carver in the southern United States be useful to farmers in Africa, Europe, and Asia?

   _____

   _____

George Washington Carver

A Soapy Success Story

Materials: 15 mL peanut oil, 20 mL denatured ethyl alcohol, 15 mL sodium hydroxide (NaOH, 40% solution), 50 g salt (NaCl), water, two 250 mL heat-resistant beakers, hot plate, two hot pads, two tongue depressors, safety goggles, paper towels, two test tubes with stoppers

Soap was one of the more than three hundred useful products that George Washington Carver manufactured from peanuts. This was possible because peanuts contain a great deal of oil. You can see this oil if you crush a peanut against a paper towel. In the following activity you will make your own soap from commercially prepared peanut oil.

Fats and oils can be converted into soap by the chemical reaction at the right, known as *saponification*. In this reaction, a strong base such as sodium hydroxide (NaOH) is used to break molecules of fats and oils into smaller molecules. The products of this reaction are glycerol and soap.

$$\text{Fat} \quad + \quad \begin{array}{c}\text{sodium}\\\text{hydroxide}\end{array} \longrightarrow \quad \text{soap} \quad + \quad \text{glycerol}$$

$$
\begin{array}{l}
CH_2O - \overset{\overset{O}{\|}}{C} - C_{17}H_{35} \\[4pt]
CHO - \overset{\overset{O}{\|}}{C} - C_{17}H_{35} + 3NaOH \longrightarrow 3C_{17}H_{35}CO_2^-Na^+ + \\[4pt]
CH_2O - \underset{\underset{O}{\|}}{C} - C_{17}H_{35}
\end{array}
\qquad
\begin{array}{l}
CH_2OH \\[4pt]
CHOH \\[4pt]
CH_2OH
\end{array}
$$

Making Your Soap

1. Put on safety goggles.

2. Pour 150 mL of water into one of the beakers. Add 50 g of salt (NaCl) and stir with a tongue depressor. Set this beaker aside.

3. Pour 10 mL of peanut oil into the other beaker. Add 20 mL of denatured alcohol to dissolve the oil and stir. (**Safety Note:** Denatured alcohol is poisonous.)

4. Carefully add 15 mL of the 40% NaOH solution to the peanut oil-alcohol mixture. (**Safety Note:** NaOH is highly caustic and can cause serious burns. If you spill any on your skin or clothing, flush the affected area with water for at least five minutes. Report any spills to your teacher immediately.)

5. Using the hot plate, slowly heat the mixture over low to medium heat. Use a tongue depressor to stir it until it becomes a thick paste. When the mixture has thickened or begins foaming, use a hot pad to remove it from the heat. Continue stirring for a few moments. (**Safety Note:** The hot mixture contains NaOH. Stir carefully to avoid spills and splashes.)

George Washington Carver

A Soapy Success Story (continued)

6. Place the beaker of salt water that was set aside in Step 2 on the hot plate. Increase the heat. When the water boils, carefully scrape the pasty mass from Step 5 into the hot salty water. Stir until it is well mixed. Turn off the heat and use a hot pad to remove the mixture. Set it aside to cool. This step is called "salting out." As the mixture cools, you will see blobs of soap form.

7. When the mixture is fully cooled, use a clean tongue depressor to skim out your newly prepared soap. Place the soap on a paper towel, and carefully rinse it with clean water. Transfer the rinsed soap to another paper towel to dry.

Testing Your Soap

8. Fill two test tubes approximately one-third full of water. Add 2 to 3 drops of peanut oil to each.

9. Add a little of your soap to one test tube. Add nothing to the other. Stopper the tops of the test tubes and shake each one. Observe and describe the results.

_____

_____

_____

_____

10. What do your observations suggest about the way soap works?

_____

_____

_____

_____

11. How is the soap you made different from the soap you are used to? How is it similar?

_____

_____

_____

_____

George Washington Carver

Plant Doctor, Soil Doctor

Materials: pencil

Plants depend on the soil to provide nutrients for healthy growth. If the soil is lacking in any of the important nutrients, plants growing there will be weakened by nutrient deficiency diseases. The six most important nutrients for plant growth, in order of importance, are: nitrogen, phosphorus, potassium, calcium, magnesium, and sulfur.

George Washington Carver understood the needs of plants and taught farmers to manage the soil in order to produce abundant crops. He thought soil should be fertilized scientifically to add the nutrients that were lacking. He also emphasized that farmers should plant crops appropriate to the type and condition of the soil on their farms. For example, in areas where the soil was low on nitrogen, Carver suggested planting legumes, which add nitrogen to the soil.

In order to select appropriate crops and fertilizers, farmers need to know what their soil contains. Scientific soil analysis was made available to farmers in the United States through the land grant college system developed in the late 1800's. Agricultural experiment stations were set up so that farmers could consult them about soil management, pest control, and other problems. George Washington Carver performed soil analysis in his laboratory in Tuskegee, Alabama, and made recommendations to farmers.

Because chemical fertilizers were expensive and difficult to obtain in rural areas, Carver recommended that farmers use available materials for fertilizers. The materials included plant and animal wastes that are commonly found in farm areas. These materials decay when mixed into soil and their nutrients then become available to plants. Some of the materials that Carver might have recommended, and the nutrients they provide, are listed below. Use this information to answer the questions on the following page.

Material	Nutrients
corn stalks	carbon
eggshells	calcium
hay (grasses and legumes)	carbon, nitrogen, phosphorus, potassium
pine needles	carbon, nitrogen, phosphorus, potassium, iron
straw	carbon, nitrogen, potassium
wood ashes	potassium, calcium
food scraps	nitrogen
leaves	carbon, nitrogen, phosphorus potassium
animal manure	nitrogen, phosphorus, potassium, sulfur, calcium, magnesium, iron
blood meal	nitrogen
bone meal	phosphorus
cottonseed meal	nitrogen

George Washington Carver

Plant Doctor, Soil Doctor *(continued)*

1. Are there any materials listed on the previous page that contain all of the most important plant nutrients? If so, list the materials and nutrients.

   _____

   _____

2. Are there any materials listed on the previous page that do not contain any of the essential plant nutrients? If so, list the materials and nutrients.

   _____

   _____

3. Which materials, or combinations of materials, can be used to obtain the three most important plant nutrients?

   _____

   _____

   _____

4. Suppose you are a farmer and have just received these results from your soil analysis.

Soil Analysis Results

Nutrient	Low	Medium	High
Nitrogen			√
Phosphorus	√		
Potassium	√		
Calcium	√		
Magnesium		√	
Sulphur		√	

Develop a strategy for enriching the soil on your farm using the materials discussed on the previous page. Describe your strategy and explain your reasoning.

_____

_____

_____

The Celts

Buyd Ur—Butter

The **Celts** (pronounced KELTS), or Celtae, were ancient indigenous peoples who lived in western and central Europe from 1000 B.C. to 100 B.C. They inhabited areas of modern-day Ireland, Scotland, England, France, Germany, Austria, Spain, Portugal, and Holland. Descendants of the Celts still live in Europe and many other parts of the world. Today, people living in some rural areas of Ireland and Scotland still use many traditional technologies developed by the Celts.

The women and men of the Celtic culture developed a food technology that surprised the ancient Romans who encountered Celtic settlements. One of these technologies involved the making of butter. The Romans had not known of butter until they came into contact with the Celts. Roman writers recorded that the Celts made butter from cream in churns that consisted of hollow cylinders without handles. Cream was poured into the churn and agitated until it became butter. The Celts improved on the churn design over time. The illustrations at the right show variations in the design of butter churns found at various locations in Ireland.

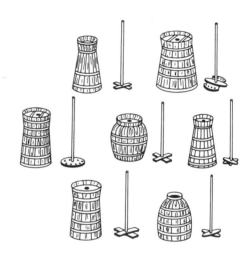

Making butter was very labor-intensive and large quantities of milk were needed to produce cream, the starting material. Because of this, the Celts used butter to pay tithings or taxes to their chiefs. The word "butter" is formed from the Celtic words *buyd* meaning "chiefs" and *ur* meaning "food."

Butter is made from milk by first isolating the cream, which is about 10% by volume. The cream is then agitated so that lumps of butter begin to form. Butter, then, can be thought of as one step beyond "whipped" cream. With further shaking or stirring, the lumps bind together to form a mass of butter. The liquid that remains is known as buttermilk.

Chemically, butter is formed when the protective protein cover of the tiny fat globules in milk are disrupted by agitation. This disruption liberates the fat globules and allows them to unite with other fat globules to form larger fat masses or lumps of butter. The disrupted outer protein coatings remain in the liquid (buttermilk) along with excluded water. The table below shows the chemical composition of milk, cream, butter, and buttermilk.

Constituents	Milk	Cream	Butter	Buttermilk
Water	87.0%	56.0 %	16.0 %	91.0 %
Fat	3.9%	39.8 %	80.6 %	0.4 %
Protein	3.5%	2.2 %	0.6 %	3.4 %
Lactose	4.9%	3.3 %	0.4 %	4.5 %
Ash	0.7%	0.5 %	2.4 %	0.7 %
Calcium (mg/100g)	118.0 mg	75.0 mg	20.0 mg	0.0 mg

The Celts

Questions for Critical Thinking

1. What background knowledge did you have about butter before reading the material on the previous page? Include personal observations and information you may have gotten from the media.

_____

_____

_____

_____

2. Before Celtic women and men knew how to make butter, they used milk and cream extensively. The "discovery" of butter may have been accidental or otherwise. Imagine and describe how the Celts might have discovered butter.

_____

_____

_____

_____

3. Nutritionists recommend drinking milk because it is high in protein. Where is the protein in milk? In the space at the right, draw a simple picture of how you envision protein and fat arranged in milk.

4. Using the table and information on the previous page, describe what happens to the water, fat, and protein as cream is changed into butter. Support your answer with data from the table.

_____

_____

_____

_____

The Celts

The Chemistry of Butter

Materials: two liters of non-homogenized, pasteurized, full cream with no additives, two jars with lids (one-pint or half-liter size), six pieces of litmus paper (3 red, 3 blue), heavy brown paper (e.g., from a grocery bag) at least 30 cm by 20 cm, nitric acid (1-molar solution) in dropper bottle, five test plates, safety goggles

In this activity, you will simulate the method the Celts used to make *buyd ur*, and then experimentally investigate several of the chemical processes involved in butter production. Your teacher will determine how to obtain cream, the starting material.

Making *Buyd Ur*

To begin the activity, you will simulate the early Celtic method of butter production, using jars as churns. Your group will measure and compare the amount of time it takes for soured cream and fresh cream to become butter. (Soured cream can be prepared by leaving cream to sit in a warm place for at least 24 hours.)

1. Prepare two jars as churns, one containing 500 mL of "sweet" or fresh cream, the other containing 500 mL of soured cream. All cream should be at room temperature. Make sure the lids are fastened securely. Label the jars appropriately.

2. Note the starting time and begin agitating the cream by shaking the jars. Keep the contents of each jar in constant motion. Pass the jar around so that each member of your group has a chance to agitate the cream. Eventually you will see the cream thicken, become lumpy, and suddenly form one lump of butter surrounded by buttermilk. Note the time that this last change occurs.

   Which type of cream do you think the Celts used most often to make *buyd ur*? Why?

   _____

   _____

Investigating Butter Chemistry

3. Use litmus paper to test the acidity of *all* ingredients and products used in Steps 1 and 2. If the substance is acidic, it will turn blue litmus paper red and not affect red litmus paper. If it is basic, it will turn red litmus paper blue and not affect blue litmus paper. If the substance is neutral, neither type of paper will change color. Record results below.

Substance	Result of Litmus-Paper Test
Milk	
Cream	
Soured Cream	
Butter	
Buttermilk	

The Chemistry of Butter (*continued*)

4. Did you find the souring effect to be acidic, basic, or neutral? What does this tell you about other foods with a sour taste?

   _____

5. To test for fat content, place a small amount (about the size of a pea) of each substance from Steps 1 and 2 on the brown paper. Keep each substance as far away from the others as possible. Let the paper dry until all liquids have evaporated. Fat will be indicated by a greasy ring around the substance. Record your results below.

Substance	Result of Brown-Paper Test for Fat
Milk	
Cream	
Soured Cream	
Butter	
Buttermilk	

6. Did the buttermilk contain fat? Why or why not?

   _____

7. Put on safety goggles. To test for protein content, place pea-sized samples of each substance on separate test plates. Add two drops of nitric acid to each sample. (**Safety Note:** Nitric acid causes burns. If you spill any on yourself, flush the area with water and inform your teacher.) If the sample turns yellow, the substance contains protein. Record your results below, noting the intensity of the yellow color for each substance.

Substance	Result of Nitric-Acid Test for Protein
Milk	
Cream	
Soured Cream	
Butter	
Buttermilk	

8. Rank the five substances in order of protein content. Do your results support the information shown in the table on the first page of this unit?

   _____

9. With the understanding you now have of the butter-making process, explain the varying amounts of protein you observed.

   _____

Chu Shih-Chieh

The History of a Triangle

Pascal's Triangle is a famous arithmetic triangle that contains number patterns occurring in algebra, geometry, and nature. It is named for the French mathematician, Blaise Pascal, who lived from 1623 to 1662. However, the so-called Pascal's Triangle was discovered some 500 years before Pascal ever lived.

In the year 1303, the Chinese mathematician **Chu Shih-Chieh** (CHU Shee Chee) displayed the famous triangle at the beginning of his book *Precious Mirror of the Four Elements*. The illustration at the right shows the triangle as it originally appeared. Chu Shih-Chieh did not even claim credit for discovering the triangle. He described it as the *ku-fa* ("old method") for finding binomial coefficients. For almost two centuries before Chu Shih-Chieh, Chinese mathematicians had known of this triangular pattern for calculating binomial coefficients.

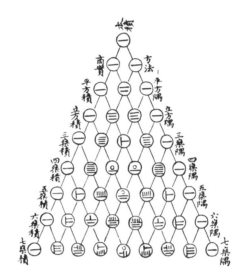

Chu Shih-Chieh was the last and greatest mathematician of the golden age of Chinese mathematics during the Sung Dynasty. Historians have described him as one of the greatest mathematicians of all time. However, very little is known about the personal life of Chu Shih-Chieh. The actual dates of his birth and death are not known. He was a resident of Yen-shan, near modern-day Beijing, but he spent over twenty years of his life traveling extensively in China as a renowned mathematician and teacher. Students flocked to study under Chu Shih-Chieh.

His two most important mathematical books were *Introduction to Mathematical Studies,* written in 1299 as an introductory textbook, and *Precious Mirror of the Four Elements*, written in 1303. The four "elements" in *Precious Mirror*—heaven, earth, man, and matter—represent four unknowns in a single equation. Both books disappeared for a time and later reappeared in Korea and Japan, as well as in China. The books of Chu Shih-Chieh strongly influenced the development of mathematics in Asia.

Precious Mirror of the Four Elements marks the peak in the development of Chinese algebra. It deals with simultaneous equations, Pascal's Triangle, and the solution of equations with exponents as high as fourteen. The method described by Chu Shih-Chieh for solving equations of degree fourteen is now commonly known as the Horner method, named for a nineteenth-century mathematician. So, although Chu Shih-Chieh was probably the first mathematician to publish Pascal's Triangle and the Horner method, his name is not associated with either discovery. Chu Shih-Chieh's significant contributions to mathematics remain largely anonymous.

Chu Shih-Chieh

Questions for Critical Thinking

1. Why do you think Chu Shih-Chieh never achieved the fame of Pascal or Horner by having a mathematical discovery named after him?

   _____

   _____

   _____

2. The first seven rows of Pascal's Triangle are shown at the right. The entries at the ends of the rows are always 1. Other entries are found by adding the two numbers to the left and right above the desired entry. Write the next two rows of Pascal's Triangle in the spaces provided.

```
                1
              1   1
            1   2   1
          1   3   3   1
        1   4   6   4   1
      1   5  10  10   5   1
    1   6  15  20  15   6   1
```

   _____

   _____

3. The **triangular numbers** form a sequence that occurs in algebra, geometry, and nature. The triangular numbers are 1, 3, 6, 10, 15, and so on. Find the next two numbers in the sequence and describe the pattern in words.

   _____

   _____

   _____

   _____

4. Find the triangular numbers in Pascal's Triangle. Circle them.

5. Describe at least one other pattern that you see in Pascal's Triangle.

   _____

   _____

   _____

   _____

Chu Shih-Chieh

Pascal's Triangle and Binomial Expansion

Materials: pencil

In algebra, much time and effort is spent working with **binomials**. A binomial is an expression with two terms, such as $3x + 1$ or $2a^2 + b$. When binomials are squared, cubed, or raised to higher powers, several patterns emerge. Chu Shih-Chieh wrote about these patterns seven centuries ago.

1. Calculate $(a + b)^2$. (This is often called the **expansion** of $(a + b)^2$.)

   _____

2. Look at the coefficients of the terms in $(a + b)^2$. Where do these numbers occur in Pascal's Triangle?

   _____

   _____

3. Calculate $(a + b)^3$. (Hint: Multiply your result from Question 1 by $a + b$.)

   _____

4. Look at the coefficients of the terms in $(a + b)^3$. Where do these numbers occur in Pascal's Triangle?

   _____

   _____

5. Use Pascal's Triangle to help you write the expansion of $(a + b)^4$ without actually doing any multiplication.

   _____

6. Chu Shih-Chieh calculated the coefficients for the expansion of $(a + b)^8$ in his book *Precious Mirror of the Four Elements*. Use Pascal's Triangle to write this expansion.

   _____

7. In general, which row of Pascal's Triangle would you use to help you write the expansion of $(a + b)^n$?

   _____

   _____

Chu Shih-Chieh

Protein Combo Plate

Materials: pencil, food cutouts from a magazine (optional)

People who follow strict vegetarian diets use food combinations to help them get the protein they need. Combinations are necessary because plant proteins do not have all eight of the essential amino acids that humans need to build healthy tissues. Rice and wheat for example, lack the amino acids lysine and isoleucine. Corn lacks lysine, isoleucine, and tryptophan. However, foods such as nuts and beans contain the missing amino acids. If these foods are eaten together with rice, wheat, or corn, one's total protein needs are met.

Food combinations can be looked at mathematically. In fact, the number patterns that occur when working with mathematical combinations are found in the rows of Chu Shih-Chieh's (Pascal's) Triangle.

1. If you have a dish of beans and a dish of rice, there are four possible food combinations, mathematically speaking. There is the option of having nothing at all, the beans only, the rice only, or both foods. These combinations can be organized by how many items are in each combination. For example, with one item, there are two possible combinations: beans only and rice only. Complete the following table.

Number of Items	0	1	2
Possible Combinations			

2. Suppose you have servings of rice, beans, and corn. List all possible combinations and complete the table below. (Cutouts from a magazine may be helpful.)

Number of Items	0	1	2	3
Possible Combinations				

Which of the above combinations provide a person's complete protein needs?

_____

3. What do you notice about the numbers in the "Possible Combinations" rows above?

_____

4. Suppose you have servings of rice, beans, corn, and wheat. How many combinations are possible using exactly two of these items? (You should be able to get this number from Pascal's Triangle.)

_____

Name _____ Date _____

Jewel Plummer Cobb

Cells Out of Control

D r. Jewel Plummer Cobb, an African-American biologist, is known for her studies in the field of cancer-cell physiology. Her basic research on the growth and development of cancer cells has been important in the effort to find effective cancer treatments. Cancer cells from many types of tumors were cultured in her laboratory. These cancer-cell cultures were used to test a wide variety of newly-synthesized anti-cancer drugs. One of these drugs was *methotrexate*. It is now widely used to treat many cancerous conditions, including lung cancer and childhood leukemia.

The many diseases known as cancers have one thing in common. They all involve cells that divide when they should not. Uncontrolled cell division results in a disorganized mass of cells known as a *tumor*. The illustration at the right compares the growth of normal skin cells and cancerous skin cells in glass culture dishes. Cell cultures like these, whether grown in test tubes, flasks, or dishes, are said to have been grown *in vitro*, Latin for "in glass."

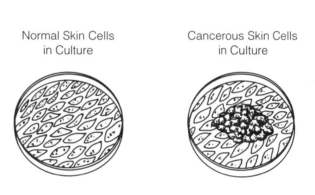

Normal Skin Cells in Culture   Cancerous Skin Cells in Culture

Cancer cells also can be studied *in vivo*. *In vivo* cancer studies involve taking cell samples from tumors growing in people or animals. Dr. Cobb tested tumor-cell samples from people undergoing cancer treatments to find out which anti-cancer drugs their tumor cells were most sensitive to. This information was then used to help the patient's physician find the most effective combination of drugs to treat the cancer.

Dr. Cobb also conducted extensive research on melanomas—cancers of the skin's pigment cells. These pigment cells, known as *melanocytes*, produce the pigment *melanin*. Melanocytes are located above the lowest skin layer (the dermis), as shown in the cross-section of the skin illustrated at the right. Melanin pigment made by the melanocytes is packaged into pigment-containing organelles that are then transferred into the newly forming cells of the epidermis, the uppermost skin layer. The variety of human skin tones is related to the density of pigment-containing organelles in these cells. Dr. Cobb's melanoma research was designed to study the processes that take place in cancerous melanocytes with the goal of finding a way to control their rapid growth throughout the body.

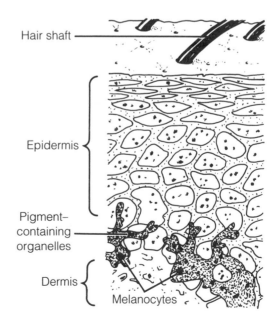

Hair shaft

Epidermis

Pigment–containing organelles

Dermis

Melanocytes

Multiculturalism in Mathematics, Science, and Technology

Jewel Plummer Cobb

Cells Out of Control *(continued)*

Dr. Cobb traces her interest in science to her high school biology class, where she first learned to use a microscope. The microscope enabled her to see an entirely new and fascinating world. By her junior year in high school, Cobb had decided to become a biology teacher. After high school, she enrolled at the University of Michigan, where she excelled in her science courses. However, she left after three semesters because of the segregated housing and campus facilities. Cobb transferred to Talladega College in Alabama and graduated in 1944. While in graduate school at New York University, she decided to pursue a career in research and college teaching. After receiving her doctorate, she began the cancer-cell work for which she is best known. Dr. Cobb maintained an active research schedule for thirty-one years and also became a prominent college administrator, serving as President of California State University, Fullerton. Having retired from that position in 1990, she now holds the post of President Emeritus.

Questions for Critical Thinking

1. Study the illustration of the two culture dishes on the previous page. Explain the differences between the cancerous and non-cancerous cells.

_____

_____

2. The pigment melanin is found in the skin, fur, and feathers of animals. Why do you think this is the case?

_____

_____

3. When human skin is repeatedly exposed to the sun, it may darken or "tan." How do you think this can take place?

_____

_____

4. Many animals, such as frogs, fish, and octopuses, can change color quickly. These color changes are useful for camouflage when the animal moves to different surroundings. What might be taking place to make these color changes possible? Do you think this process is different from tanning? Why or why not?

_____

_____

_____

Jewel Plummer Cobb

Analyzing Cell Growth

Materials: pencil

Dr. Jewel Plummer Cobb's research involved growing many different cultures of normal and cancerous cells. Two graphs of cell growth are shown below. Study the graphs. Then use the graphs to answer the questions below.

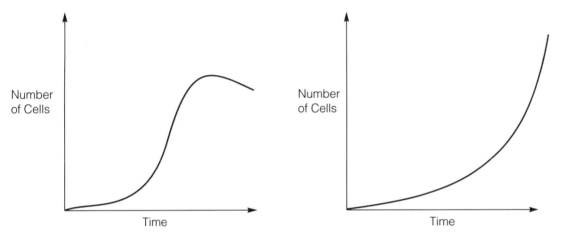

1. Compare the two graphs. How are they they same? How are they different?

_____

_____

_____

2. Which graph do you think shows the growth of normal cells? Explain your answer.

_____

_____

_____

3. Which graph do you think shows the growth of cancerous cells? Explain your answer.

_____

_____

_____

4. Write an appropriate title under each graph. Add labels to the graphs to describe what is happening in each.

Jewel Plummer Cobb

A Melanoma Experiment

Materials: pencil

In 1956, Dr. Cobb wanted to find out why melanomas (cancerous tumors of skin pigment cells) did not respond to standard radiation treatments with radium and X-rays. She decided to test cells from mouse melanomas. When she examined mouse melanoma tumors closely, she found that they had areas containing large amounts of the pigment melanin and areas containing less melanin. To perform her experiment, she took tissue slices of both types. She then exposed each type to varying doses of X-rays and tried growing the treated tissues *in vitro*.

The following list summarizes Dr. Cobb's results. Study the information and use it to answer the questions below.

X-ray Dose	More-pigmented Tissues	Less-pigmented Tissues
No X-rays	Grew	Grew
Low	Grew	Grew
Medium	Grew	Did not grow
High	Grew	Did not grow
Very high	Did not grow	Did not grow

1. What can you conclude from the results of Dr. Cobb's experiment? Explain your answer.

_____

_____

_____

_____

_____

2. How do Dr. Cobb's results relate to the research question she sought to answer?

_____

_____

_____

_____

_____

Charles Richard Drew

Blood Banks: Assessing the Fluid of Life

Millions of people are alive today because of an African-American surgeon's pioneering work with blood. Anyone who has received a blood transfusion, whether in war or peace, probably owes his or her life to **Dr. Charles Richard Drew** (1904–1950). During World War II, Dr. Drew was the world's leading authority on the preservation of human blood for transfusion.

In 1930, scientist Karl Landsteiner received the Nobel Prize for his work on blood typing. Dr. Drew realized the implications of these research findings: to perform blood transfusions successfully, the donor and the recipient must have the same blood type (A, B, AB, or O) and their blood must be compatible.

However, Dr. Drew recognized another critical problem: the need to preserve and store blood. He concentrated his research on the use of plasma—the liquid portion of blood. Dr. Drew's research provided evidence that blood plasma could be stored without spoiling for much longer periods than whole blood. The diagram at the right shows the composition of whole blood. Dr. Drew's work on plasma storage made blood banks practical for the first time. Although the idea of a blood bank had been explored by Soviet scientists, the problem of blood spoilage had kept blood banks from practical use.

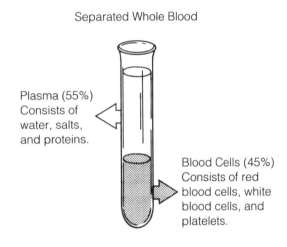

Separated Whole Blood

Plasma (55%) Consists of water, salts, and proteins.

Blood Cells (45%) Consists of red blood cells, white blood cells, and platelets.

The early part of Dr. Drew's career was marked by a love of sports as well as medicine. He graduated in 1926 from Amherst College where he was a football star. Although he could have had a career in athletics, he always dreamed of one day becoming a medical doctor. In 1928, he was accepted at McGill University Medical School in Canada and soon became an outstanding student. At McGill University he met Dr. John Beattie, an English physician and professor of anatomy. Both Beattie and Drew became interested in investigating the problems associated with blood transfusions. At that time, transfusions were only possible if fresh blood could be obtained from a closely-related donor.

In 1938, Dr. Drew received a fellowship to do graduate research at Columbia University. There, he began his research on techniques to preserve blood for later use. In 1944, Dr. Drew was appointed Chief of Staff at Freedmen's Hospital in Washington, D. C. At the same time, he was Head of Surgery at Howard University.

The brilliant pioneering work of Dr. Charles Drew will long be remembered in every blood bank around the world. The results of his untiring efforts toward the preservation of human blood for emergency use have saved many lives. Ironically, Dr. Drew was involved in a car accident on April 1, 1950, and died because of a desperate need for a blood transfusion.

Charles Richard Drew

Questions for Critical Thinking

1. Give at least one important reason why Karl Landsteiner's work on blood typing was significant to Dr. Drew's research.

_____

_____

_____

2. Why is a "blood bank" such an important idea?

_____

_____

3. In addition to blood-group compatibility, what precautions might be taken before a doctor considers a blood transfusion?

_____

_____

4. Why was Dr. Drew's research so important during his time?

_____

_____

_____

5. Why is blood sometimes referred to as the "fluid of life"?

_____

_____

_____

6. How has Dr. Drew's blood research affected public health today?

_____

_____

_____

Charles Richard Drew

Keeping Blood Fresh

Materials: pencil

Dr. Charles Richard Drew developed his techniques of plasma storage by performing various laboratory experiments. He identified and tested variables such as storage temperature and preservative concentration. In this activity, you will interpret data from blood storage experiments and come to your own conclusions about the best conditions for keeping whole blood fresh.

Experiment A (Temperature and Blood Storage)

The graph at the right shows six data points from an experiment with whole blood. In this experiment, whole blood samples were stored at 4°C and at room temperature (approximately 25°C). The length of time it took for each blood sample to separate was marked on the graph. Study the graph and answer the questions below.

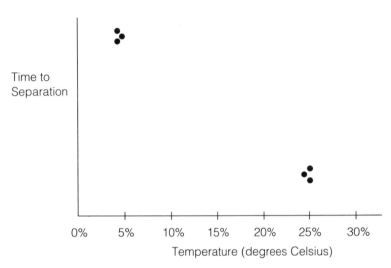

1. What effect does temperature have on blood decomposition?

   _____

   _____

   _____

   _____

2. Is there a "best" temperature for storing blood? Why or why not?

   _____

   _____

   _____

   _____

Charles Richard Drew

Keeping Blood Fresh (continued)

Experiment B (Fresh Blood Preservation)

The graph at the right shows several data points from an experiment with whole blood. In this experiment, whole blood samples were stored at the same temperature with different concentrations of sodium citrate, a preservative. The length of time it took for each blood sample to separate was marked on the graph. Study the graph and answer the questions below.

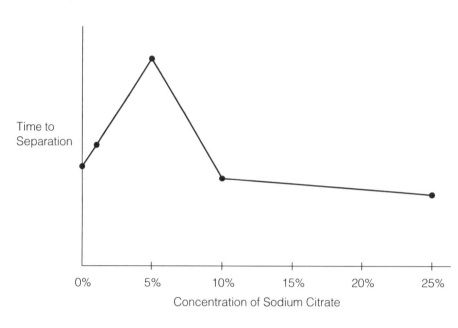

3. What effect does sodium citrate have on blood decomposition? Explain.

   _____

   _____

4. What concentration of sodium citrate was the best preservative? Explain.

   _____

   _____

5. Based on your interpretations of Experiments A and B, what do you think would be the best conditions for preserving whole blood? What do you think would be the worst conditions?

   _____

   _____

   _____

   _____

   _____

The Ancient Egyptians I

Coordination with Coordinates

 bout 5000 years ago, African artists were decorating a tomb in southern Egypt. The plan was to paint the pharaoh's picture on the wall, twice actual size. The artists were working from a small sketch. One of them may have said, "Let's draw a grid of small squares on the sketch and a grid of large squares on the wall. Then we can transfer the drawing, square by square, from the small sketch to the large wall." That is how the idea of proportional drawings was born. The principle of similar figures had been discovered. In transferring the drawing, angles and curvature would remain the same, and lengths in the large figure would be proportional to lengths in the small figure. This principle is still used today when small photographs are taken of large objects.

The Egyptian artists had another idea. Since pharaohs, male or female, were supposed to be perfect, the artists decided on proportions for the "ideal" body. Allowing 22 squares for the full height, the ideal proportions, measured in squares from the ground, were as follows.

ankle	$1\frac{1}{4}$ squares
knee	$7\frac{1}{4}$ squares
waist	$13\frac{1}{2}$ squares
chest	17 squares
mouth	20 squares
top of head	22 squares

Classical Greek sculptors studied with Egyptian artists and took these idealized proportions back to Greece. Early Greek statues are true to this Egyptian ideal.

Ancient Egyptian architects also made plans that used the idea of square grids. These architects put a grid of small squares on their plans for a structure. Then the engineers built the structure from the plan, square by square. No doubt they located a point on the plan by counting the number of squares over from the side and the number of squares up from the bottom.

That was just a step away from making graphs with rectangular coordinates. Rectangular coordinates locate a point by giving the horizontal distance and the vertical distance from fixed perpendicular axes. It is not known who took that first step. However, it is known that as long ago as 2750 B.C. rectangular coordinates were used in Africa. That was the year the first African pyramid was built at Saqqara, Egypt.

The Ancient Egyptians I

Coordination with Coordinates *(continued)*

The pyramid at Saqqara was surrounded by temples and courtyards for religious services. For one of the temples, the architects designed a curved section for the roof. They sketched the detail for the curve on a piece of limestone. After the roof was finished, the foreman probably threw away the detail.

About 4600 years later, the architect's detail was discovered. It was still next to the curved piece for the temple roof. The coordinates were written in ancient Egyptian script as shown here. Vertical coordinates are given in cubits—the length of a pharaoh's forearm from the elbow to the end of the middle finger. Subdivisions of the cubit are palms and fingers. There are 4 fingers to a palm and 7 palms to 1 cubit. The horizontal coordinates are shown as evenly spaced and can be taken from context to be 28 fingers apart.

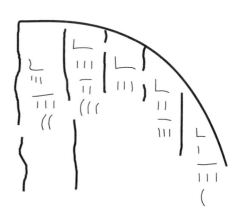

Questions for Critical Thinking

1. Are there 7 of your palms to your cubit, the length of your forearm?

   _____

2. What fraction of a cubit is 1 finger?

   _____

3. Do you think any pharaoh actually fit the ideal proportions that the artists established? Why or why not?

   _____

   _____

   _____

4. The base length of the Great Pyramid is accurate to 1 part in 2500. How do you think the ancient Egyptians achieved this accuracy?

   _____

   _____

   _____

The Ancient Egyptians I

The Ideal Figure

Materials: pencil, tape measure (or two meter sticks taped to the wall), graph paper

The concept of the ideal proportions for the body of a pharaoh was introduced by ancient Egyptian artists. Although the "ideal" figure is a matter of personal opinion, it can be fun to compare your own proportions with the ideal developed for pharaohs.

1. Work with a partner to record the height, measured up from the ground, of the body parts listed in the table below. Record your results in the table, consistently using either centimeters or inches.

2. The Egyptians used 22 squares for a person's total height. You can set up a proportion as follows to find the number of squares, x, that represent the height of each body part.

$$\frac{\text{height of body part}}{\text{total height}} = \frac{x}{22}$$

Solving for x gives the number of squares needed to represent the height of the body part. For example, one student is 66 inches tall and has an ankle height of 3 inches. The proportion $\frac{3}{66} = \frac{x}{22}$ gives $x = 1$, so one square should be allotted for the height of the ankle.

Set up proportions as shown above to calculate the number of squares required to represent the height of each body part. Record your results in the table. You can now compare your own proportions to those of the "ideal" pharaoh.

Body Part	Height from Ground (cm or in.)	Number of Squares	"Ideal" Number of Squares
Ankle			
Knee			
Waist			
Chest			
Mouth			
Top of Head			

3. Use graph paper and the data from the "Number of Squares" column of the table to make a scale drawing of your body. Be sure to use 22 squares of the graph paper for the total height. (You may also want to sketch an "ideal pharaoh" alongside the drawing of your body to see how the proportions compare. Use the figures in the " 'Ideal' Number of Squares" column.)

Multiculturalism in Mathematics, Science, and Technology

Name _____   Date _____

Egyptian Coordinates

Materials: pencil, graph paper

The drawing at the right is a reproduction of a piece of limestone. It gives the coordinates for a curved structure. The coordinates are written in ancient Egyptian script. However, they are easy to read because the writing is actually a series of pictures.

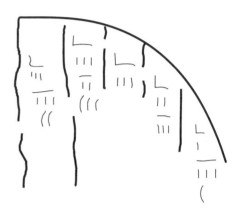

For example, the leftmost column of coordinates shows a picture of a bent arm (the cubit) with 3 tallies under it. This means there are 3 cubits. Under this is a straight line (the palm) with 3 tallies under it. This means there are 3 palms. Finally, there are two bent lines (fingers), meaning there are two fingers. Thus, the reading for the first vertical coordinate is 3 cubits, 3 palms, and 2 fingers. Note that the horizontal coordinates are taken as 28 fingers apart.

1. Fill in the middle column of the table below by reading the Egyptian coordinates.

2. Use 1 cubit = 7 palms, 1 palm = 4 fingers, and 1 cubit = 28 fingers to find the vertical coordinates in term of fingers. Record your results in the rightmost column of the table.

Horizontal Coordinate (in fingers)	Vertical Coordinate	Vertical Coordinate (in fingers)
0	3 cubits, 3 palms, 2 fingers	
28		
56		
84		
112		
140	No entry	0

3. Plot the coordinates on a sheet of graph paper.

4. Connect the points as smoothly as possible and compare your graph with the above drawing of the curve.

The Ancient Egyptians II

Egyptian Numerals and Arithmetic

F ive-thousand years ago, the ancient Egyptians used a base-ten system of numerals. The numerals were written with pictures called hieroglyphics. For the numbers 1 through 9, they simply used tally marks, with one vertical mark representing 1, two vertical marks representing 2, and so on. Symbols for the powers of ten were as shown in the following chart.

1	10	100	1,000	10,000	100,000

Using these symbols, Egyptian numbers were written right to left. Some examples are shown below.

3

23

32

702

2,105

3,000

10,011

41,023

Compared to modern numerals, this system could result in lengthy expressions. However, Egyptian numerals did have certain advantages. For instance, to multiply a number by 10, one simply changed each symbol in the number to the next higher power of ten. The example below shows how the Egyptians would have multiplied 4,205 by 10.

4,205

4,205 X 10
= 42,050

The Egyptians also had a special method for multiplying other numbers. The method uses powers of 2. Much of Egyptian mathematics was built around powers of 2 and the ideas of doubling or halving a number.

Multiculturalism in Mathematics, Science, and Technology **61**

The Ancient Egyptians II

Questions for Critical Thinking

In Questions 1 through 5, write each number using Egyptian numerals.

1. 5

_____

2. 34

_____

3. 127

_____

4. 5,033

_____

5. 10,218

_____

6. Name at least three differences between ancient Egyptian numerals and modern numerals.

_____

_____

_____

_____

7. Like the modern number system, the Egyptian number system was based on the number 10. Historically, many number systems have been based on the numbers 5, 10, and 20. Why do you think these were common choices?

_____

_____

_____

_____

Name _____ Date _____

Egyptian Multiplication

Materials: pencil

The ancient Egyptian method of multiplication is based on doubling. To use the method, you only have to know how to multiply by 2 and add. This means that students in ancient Egypt did not have to memorize multiplication tables! Here is how to use Egyptian multiplication to calculate 11×33.

1. Begin by forming two columns (you may use the table at the right). Place the number 1 in the first row of the left column and the number 33 in the first row of the right column.

2. Double the numbers in both columns, placing the results in the second row.

3. Double the numbers in the second row and place the results in the third row. Continue the doubling process until the number in the left column is greater than, or equal to, 11.

4. Circle the numbers in the left column that add up to 11.

5. Add up the numbers in the right column that correspond to the circled numbers. This will give the desired product, 11×33. Write the addition and the final result below.

_____

Does this method work for any pair of numbers? Was it just a coincidence that there were numbers in the left column that added up to 11? Notice that the numbers in the left column are powers of 2. This method of multiplication *does* work for any pair of numbers because every positive integer can be written as a sum of powers of 2.

Use Egyptian multiplication to calculate the following. Show your work in the tables and in the blank areas provided.

6. 13×27

7. 16×42

The Ancient Egyptians II

The Very Large and the Very Small

Materials: pencil, calculator, extra sheet of paper

Suppose you had a piece of string one centimeter long and were able to double its length as often as you wished. If you performed 80 successive doublings, how long do you think the piece of string would be? Circle the choice below that you think is closest to this length.

a. The height the Empire State Building (431 m)
b. The distance from New York to San Francisco (4720 km)
c. The distance from the earth to the sun (150,000,000 km)
d. The distance to the Andromeda galaxy (20,000,000,000,000,000,000,000 km)

The concept of repeated multiplications by 2 was of interest to the ancient Egyptians. They also studied the effects of repeated divisions by 2. A problem on one papyrus asked the student to "multiply by $\frac{1}{2}$ to infinity." Today, calculators make it much easier to investigate successive doubling and halving. The following activity will give you some experience with these processes, as well as provide an answer to the question posed above.

1. Enter 1 on your calculator. Then divide by 2. Continue dividing by 2 and record your results on a separate sheet of paper every ten divisions or so. What is happening to the numbers? (Remember that many calculators display very small numbers with scientific notation. A display of 5 – 09 means 5×10^{-9} or 0.000000005.)

   _____

2. Does your calculator ever read 0?

   _____

3. Can you ever get to 0 by successive halving?

   _____

4. Clear your calculator and then enter 1. Multiply by 2. Continue multiplying by 2 and record your results on a separate sheet of paper every ten multiplications or so. What is happening to the numbers? (Remember that most calculators display very large numbers with scientific notation. A display of 3 08 means 3×10^8 or 300,000,000.)

   _____

5. What number do you get after 80 doublings?

   _____

6. What is the correct answer to the question posed at the top of this page? (Surprised?)

   _____

The Ancient Egyptians III

Aha! Egyptian Algebra

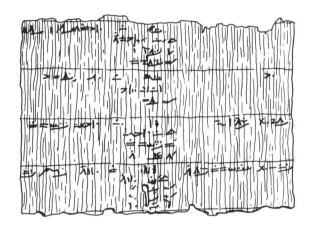

ad you lived and studied in ancient Egypt, your "paper" would have been made from a water plant called the papyrus (puh PY russ). Some of this paper-like material, also known as papyrus, has survived to this day. Perhaps the most famous mathematical papyrus was written around 1600 B.C. by a scribe named Ah-mose. A section of this papyrus is shown in the illustration at the right.

From the Ah-mose Papyrus, we know that Egyptian mathematicians had developed a type of algebra to solve practical problems. "Aha," the Egyptian word for *heap*, was used the way x is used today to represent an unknown quantity. Consequently, Egyptian algebra is sometimes called "aha calculus."

The Ah-mose Papyrus contains many examples of equations and their solutions. Although the Ah-mose Papyrus was written in a type of script, symbols were used for writing equations. For example, feet walking towards a quantity indicated addition. Feet walking away from a quantity meant subtraction. An example of an Egyptian equation, written in hieroglyphics, is shown below.

Among the Egyptian discoveries in algebra that Ah-mose recorded was the rule of **false position.** This method was used to solve equations for thousands of years, all over the world. To use false position, a trial solution value is chosen. Then, this trial solution is substituted for the unknown in the equation. Usually, the trial solution does not solve the equation. The correct solution is found by multiplying the trial value by a proportional correction factor.

The Egyptians were well aware of the need to check the solutions they obtained by false position. Ah-mose checked the results of his calculations by substituting the solutions into the original equations. This is significant in the history of mathematics as one of the earliest recorded instances of proof.

Multiculturalism in Mathematics, Science, and Technology

The Ancient Egyptians III

Questions for Critical Thinking

1. Why do you think Egyptian algebra was developed?

_____

_____

_____

_____

2. In what types of situations might the ancient Egyptians have needed algebra?

_____

_____

_____

_____

3. In the method of false position, an equation is solved by first choosing a trial solution value and then multiplying this value by a correction factor to find the true solution. Do you think there is an advantage to this method over more modern methods? Why or why not?

_____

_____

_____

_____

4. Why do you think Ah-mose recorded equations and their solutions?

_____

_____

_____

_____

_____

The Ancient Egyptians III

The Method of False Position

Materials: pencil

Here is a problem taken from the Ah-mose Papyrus. The sum of *aha* and $\frac{1}{4}$ *aha* is 15. Find *aha*. Using x for *aha*, the equation is $x + (\frac{1}{4})x = 15$. It can be solved by the method of false position as follows.

To begin, choose a trial solution value. A convenient trial value is 4, since this eliminates the fraction. Substituting 4 for x on the left side of the equation gives $4 + (\frac{1}{4})4$, or 5. However, the desired answer is 15. To get 15 from 5, one multiplies by 3. Therefore, the correction factor is 3. The correct solution is 3 times the trial value of 4, or 12.

The correct solution can also be calculated with a proportion.

$$\frac{x}{\text{trial solution value}} = \frac{\text{right side of equation}}{\text{result of substitution}}$$

The proportion gives $\frac{x}{4} = \frac{15}{5}$, so $x = \frac{15}{5}(4)$ or 12.

The Egyptians were aware of the need to prove that the solution value, when substituted into the original equation, resulted in a true statement. Substituting 12 for x in the equation $x + (\frac{1}{4})x = 15$ gives $12 + (\frac{1}{4})12 = 15$ or $12 + 3 = 15$, a true statement, so the solution checks.

Complete the steps below to solve the following problem by the method of false position. The sum of *aha* and $\frac{1}{3}$ *aha* is 21. What is the value of *aha*?

1. Use x for *aha* to write an equation for this problem. _____

2. Choose a convenient trial value for x. _____

3. Substitute this value of x into the left side of the equation. What is the result? Is the trial value the correct solution?

   _____

4. Write a proportion and solve it to find the correct value of x.

   _____

5. Substitute this value of x into the original equation to check.

   _____

6. Does the initial choice of a trial value matter? Why or why not?

   _____

Name _____   Date _____

False Position and Second-Degree Equations

Materials: pencil

The Egyptian method of false position was used to solve second-degree equations. Here is a problem involving the areas of two squares that leads to a second-degree equation.

The sum of the areas of two squares is 100 square units. The smaller of the two squares has sides $\frac{3}{4}$ the length of the sides of the larger square. What are the dimensions of the two squares?

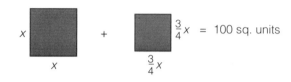

$\frac{3}{4}x = 100$ sq. units

Let x be the length of each side of the larger square. Then the sides of the smaller square each have length $\frac{3}{4}x$.

1. What is the area of the larger square in terms of x? _____

   What is the area of the smaller square in terms of x? _____

2. Write an equation for the above problem. (The variable x should appear only on the left side of the equation.)

   _____

3. To solve the equation using false position, 4 is chosen as a trial solution value. Why is 4 a convenient choice?

   _____

4. What is the result of substituting 4 for x in the left side of the equation? _____

5. By what factor must the answer to Question 4 be multiplied to get the value on the right side of the equation?

   _____

6. Your answer to Question 5 is the correction factor for the *area*. To find the correction factor for the *side lengths*, take the square root of this number. Then multiply the trial solution value, 4, by this correction factor to find the solution to the equation.

   _____

7. What are the dimensions of the two squares in the problem?

   _____

Eratosthenes

Around the World with a Measuring Tape

Have you ever wondered how scientists measure the height of a mountain, the weight of the moon, or the distance around the earth? Because of their size, objects like these cannot be weighed or measured directly. Since ancient times, men and women have tried to find other methods of calculating such data. These methods, called **indirect measurement,** often involve geometry, trigonometry, or algebra.

One of the earliest and best-known calculations of the distance around the earth was made by **Eratosthenes** (Err a TOS then ees). Eratosthenes was born in Cyrene (in present-day Libya) around 274 B.C. He was educated in Athens and then taught at the university in Alexandria after 240 B.C. He is known to have been librarian of the university and to have achieved fame as a poet.

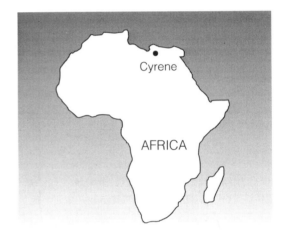

Eratosthenes was so admired that some of his contemporaries called him "the second Plato." His nickname, "Beta," may have signified that he was thought of as the second great thinker of antiquity, as the letter *beta* is the second in the Greek alphabet.

In the area of mathematics, Eratosthenes is best known for his prime-number "sieve." In order to create a list of prime numbers, Eratosthenes began by writing down a list of consecutive whole numbers greater than 1. He then went through the list and crossed off all numbers greater than 2 that were multiples of 2. Then he went back through the list, crossing off all numbers greater than 3 that were multiples of 3. Continuing the process, Eratosthenes came up with a list similar to the following: 2, 3, 4̸, 5, 6̸, 7, 8̸, 9̸.... The numbers that were not filtered out were the primes.

Eratosthenes was also very interested in geometry. In his writings, he discussed a famous problem known as the "duplication of the cube." Given a cube, the problem requires finding the appropriate edge length to create a cube with twice the volume of the given one. Eratosthenes's work summarized some of the methods used to study the problem up to that time.

By the time of his death, in about 194 B.C., the achievements of Eratosthenes justified his being called the first geographer of antiquity. At the right is a map from J. H. Breasted's *Ancient Times* that is credited to Eratosthenes. It shows the knowledge of world geography in the third century B.C.

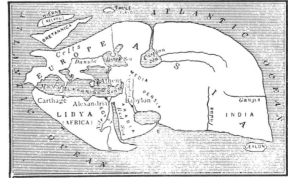

Multiculturalism in Mathematics, Science, and Technology

Eratosthenes

Questions for Critical Thinking

1. Give at least three additional examples of measurements (length, weight, distance, etc.) that must be calculated by indirect measurement.

_____

_____

_____

For the following questions, refer to Eratosthenes's map of the world at the right. You may also wish to refer to an atlas.

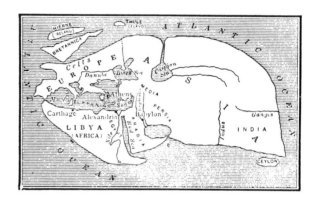

2. Which regions were mapped most accurately by Eratosthenes?

_____

_____

3. Which regions were mapped least accurately by Eratosthenes?

_____

_____

4. What parts of the earth are completely missing from Eratosthenes's map?

_____

_____

5. What do you think accounts for your answers to Questions 2, 3, and 4?

_____

_____

_____

Name _____   Date _____

Eratosthenes

The Circumference of the Earth

Materials: pencil

To calculate the circumference (distance around) the earth, Eratosthenes used the position of the sun and some basic geometry. To begin, Eratosthenes knew that on June 21, at noon, the sun cast no shadows in a town called Syene. He concluded that the sun must be directly overhead.

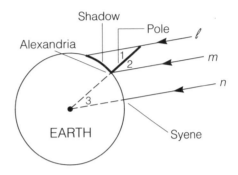

In the city of Alexandria, the sun *did* cast shadows at noon on June 21. This meant that the sun's rays were striking the earth at an angle in Alexandria.

1. In the figure, ℓ, m, and n represent the sun's rays. Because of the great distance from the sun to the earth, Eratosthenes assumed that these rays were parallel. What could Eratosthenes conclude about $\angle 1$, $\angle 2$, and $\angle 3$?

   _____

2. Using the shadow cast by a pole, Eratosthenes determined that $m\angle 1 = 7.2°$. What does this say about $m\angle 3$?

   _____

At the time of Eratosthenes's calculation, the main unit for measuring large distances was the *stadium* (plural, *stadia*). It was the distance from one end of a particular stadium to the other. Eratosthenes took the distance between Syene and Alexandria to be 5000 stadia. It is unknown how this figure was determined, but Eratosthenes may have known it from reports of travelers.

3. With this information, the following proportions can be set up. Complete the proportion on the right, in which C is the earth's circumference.

   $$\frac{m\angle 3}{360} = \frac{\text{distance from Syene to Alexandria}}{\text{circumference of the earth}} \qquad \text{or} \qquad \frac{\rule{1cm}{0.4pt}}{360} = \frac{\rule{1cm}{0.4pt}}{C}$$

   Solve this proportion for C to find the circumference of the earth in stadia.

   _____

4. It is believed that 1 stadium was about 185 meters. Complete the following.

   $C =$ _____ stadia $C =$ _____ meters $C =$ _____ kilometers

Multiculturalism in Mathematics, Science, and Technology

Eratosthenes

The Length of Africa

Materials: pencil, straightedge, protractor

Suppose you want to determine the maximum length
of the African continent. As shown on the map, this is
the greatest north-south distance one could travel in
Africa. A process of indirect measurement similar to
that used by Eratosthenes may be used to
approximate this distance.

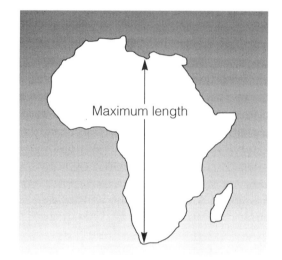

The figure at the right shows a scale drawing of the
earth, including North America, South America, and
part of Africa. Photographs from satellites make it
possible to draw such figures very accurately. Point C
is the center of the disk representing the earth.

1. Draw rays from the center of the circle to the
   northernmost and southernmost point of Africa
   on the circumference of the circle. Label the angle
   formed ∠1.

2. Use a protractor to measure ∠1.

   $m\angle 1 =$ _____

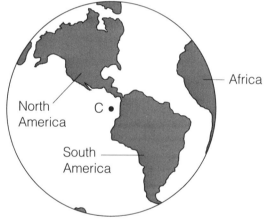

3. The circumference of the earth is very close to 40,000 km.
   Use this value to complete the proportion on the right below.

   $$\frac{m\angle 1}{360} = \frac{\text{maximum length of Africa}}{\text{circumference of the earth}} \quad \text{or} \quad \frac{}{360} = \frac{x}{}$$

4. Solve the above proportion to find x, the maximum length of Africa in kilometers.

   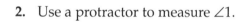
   _____

5. In the figure, what is assumed about the position of Africa in order to make the
   calculation work?

   _____

   _____

Bernardo Houssay

"Sweet" Secrets

Argentine physiologist **Dr. Bernardo Houssay** (1887–1971) is known for his work in endocrinology, the study of the body's system of endocrine glands. Endocrine glands secrete hormones that control various bodily functions. Dr. Houssay's most important work was his study of the role of the pituitary gland in the disease *diabetes mellitus*. For this work he was awarded the Nobel Prize in Medicine and Physiology in 1947.

People with *diabetes mellitus* have abnormally high levels of glucose, a simple sugar, in their blood and urine. The abnormal glucose level is caused by inadequate production or use of *insulin*, a hormone that controls the uptake of glucose into the body's cells. There is a treatment, but no cure, for this condition. People with diabetes often follow a carefully planned diet and take insulin to help stabilize their blood sugar. A simple diagram showing the relationship of insulin to body organs and other endocrine glands is shown below.

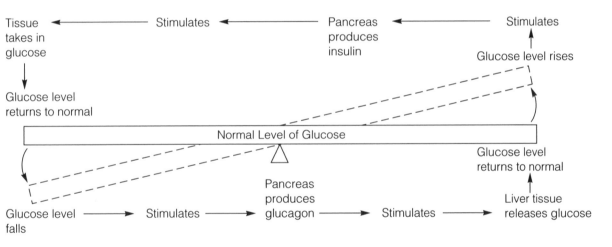

Dr. Houssay's work with diabetes built on centuries of research by other scientists. The disease has been known by medical practitioners on several continents since ancient times. The name used today was coined by Greek physicians around A.D. 200. *Mellitus*, the word for "honeyed," was used to describe the sweetness that ancient physicians detected in the urine. Many centuries later, in 1776, European chemists proved that the sweetness was due to the presence of glucose.

The first clue to how blood sugar is regulated came in 1863. Claude Bernard discovered that the liver converts glucose to glycogen and stores it. In 1889, Oskar Minkowski and Joseph von Mering discovered that diabetes could be induced in dogs by removal of the pancreas. This proved that the pancreas was the source of a substance that regulated blood sugar. In 1922, Frederick Banting and Charles Best isolated this substance, known as insulin, from pancreatic tissue. In the early 1930's, Dr. Houssay discovered that removal of the anterior lobe of the pituitary gland reduced the severity of diabetes. This proved that a substance produced by the pituitary gland was somehow involved. It is now known that the pituitary gland produces hormones that control many other endocrine glands.

Bernardo Houssay

"Sweet" Secrets *(continued)*

Bernardo Alberto Houssay was born in Buenos Aires, Argentina, on April 10, 1887. As a child, he excelled in all phases of academic studies. After graduating from the School of Pharmacy at the University of Buenos Aires, he enrolled in the medical school there. He received the M.D. degree at age 23 and briefly held a teaching post at a nearby hospital, but soon left to concentrate on research. He was then appointed professor at the Institute of Physiology, and did all of his later work there. Dr. Houssay's research combined the fields of physiology, biochemistry, and pharmacology.

Dr. Houssay, the first Latin American to win the Nobel Prize for Medicine and Physiology, also was interested in developing scientific organizations and journals in Argentina. He helped found the Argentine Association for the Advancement of Science and the *Instituto de Biologia y Medicina Experimental*. After a lifetime of work to further the advancement of science in his country and around the world, Dr. Houssay died in Buenos Aires on September 21, 1971, at age 84.

Questions for Critical Thinking

1. In the disease *diabetes mellitus*, sugar (glucose) builds up in the blood because it is not being taken up into the body's cells. What are some symptoms that a person with diabetes might experience?

   _____

   _____

2. Why do you think the pituitary gland is sometimes called the "master" gland?

   _____

   _____

3. Continued research since Houssay's time has made it possible for synthetic human insulin to be produced. It is a great improvement over insulin purified from animal glands. What are some possible reasons for this?

   _____

   _____

4. Study the diagram on the preceding page. In your own words, explain how the body works to maintain a normal level of glucose.

   _____

   _____

Bernardo Houssay

What's on the Menu?

Materials: pencil

Dr. Bernardo Houssay's research led to a better understanding of the disease *diabetes mellitus*. Today, many cases of this disease can be controlled with a carefully planned diet. In planning the diet, the total number of calories and the proportion of calories coming from fat, protein, and carbohydrates are important. However, there are other factors to consider. For example, complex carbohydrates (starches) are digested slower than simple carbohydrates (sugars). In general, foods containing carbohydrates should be spaced throughout the day, rather than eaten all at once. Food choices also need to provide the necessary vitamins and minerals.

The table below shows recommended amounts of protein, fats, and carbohydrates for people with diabetes. Total daily calorie recommendations are also shown. The appropriate number of calories depends on a person's body weight and activity level. Moderately active males, ages 13 to 17, should consume 26 to 29 calories per pound of body weight. Moderately active females, ages 13 to 17, should consume 19 to 24 calories per pound of body weight.

Calories per day	Carbohydrates (grams/day)	Proteins (grams/day)	Fats (grams/day)
1200	125	60	50
1500	150	70	70
1800	180	80	80
2200	220	90	100
2600	250	115	130
3000	300	120	145

The table below lists the amount of carbohydrates, protein, fat, and calories in many common foods.

Food	Amount	Carbohydrates	Protein	Fat	Calories
Cereals, grains, pasta	1 cup	30 grams	6 grams	trace	160
Bread, roll, tortilla	1 small	15 grams	3 grams	trace	80
Beans, peas, rice	1 cup	45 grams	9 grams	trace	240
Potato	1 small	15 grams	3 grams	trace	80
Snack crackers	6	15 grams	3 grams	5 grams	125
Lean meat, poultry, fish	3 ounces	0 grams	21 grams	9 grams	165
Regular meat, cheese	1 ounce	0 grams	7 grams	8 grams	100
Eggs	1	0 grams	7 grams	5 grams	75
Raw vegetables	1 cup	5 grams	2 grams	0 grams	25
Cooked vegetables	1 cup	10 grams	4 grams	0 grams	50
Fresh fruit or juice	1 cup	30 grams	0 grams	0 grams	120
Dried fruit	1 cup	60 grams	0 grams	0 grams	240
Lowfat milk, yogurt	1 cup	12 grams	8 grams	5 grams	120
Oil, butter, mayonnaise	1 tsp	0 grams	0 grams	5 grams	45
Snack chips	1 ounce	15 grams	3 grams	10 grams	162

Multiculturalism in Mathematics, Science, and Technology   **75**

Bernardo Houssay

What's on the Menu ? *(continued)*

1. Using the general guidelines and the food chart on the previous page, design a one-day menu for a diabetic person of your sex and body weight. Begin by calculating the number of calories required. Show your work below.

   _____

   _____

2. Write your proposed menu in the spaces provided below, keeping track of carbohydrates, protein, fat, and calories.

   Breakfast   Carbohydrates:

                                                         Protein:

                                                         Fat:

                                                         Calories:

   Lunch   Carbohydrates:

                                                         Protein:

                                                         Fat:

                                                         Calories:

   Dinner   Carbohydrates:

                                                         Protein:

                                                         Fat:

                                                         Calories:

   Snacks   Carbohydrates:

                                                         Protein:

                                                         Fat:

                                                         Calories:

3. Compare the diabetic menu that you planned to a one-day menu of what you usually eat. How are the menus the same? How are they different?

   _____

   _____

   _____

Hypatia

One of Algebra's "Parents"

ypatia (hy PAY sha), an Egyptian woman born in 370, is remembered for her life as a mathematician, scientist, and teacher. She lived in Alexandria and was a professor at the famous university there. Alexandria, located in the Nile River delta on the Mediterranean coast, attracted scholars from all over Africa, Asia, and Europe. Hypatia was considered one of the great lecturers in this center of learning.

Among Hypatia's research subjects was the geometry of the **conic sections.** Conic sections are the figures formed by the intersection of a plane and a cone. Depending on the angle of the plane, the figure formed is either a circle, an ellipse, a parabola, or a hyperbola.

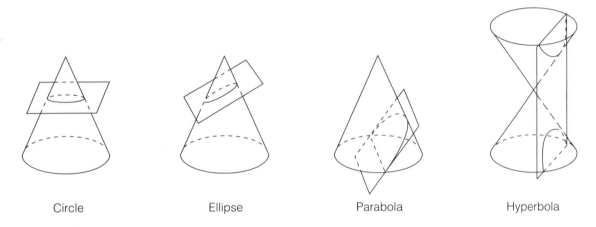

| Circle | Ellipse | Parabola | Hyperbola |

Neglected for many centuries after Hypatia's death, the importance of the conic sections was finally recognized in the seventeenth century. Today, the conic sections are used to describe the orbits of planets, the paths of comets, and the motion of rockets.

In the field of algebra, Hypatia wrote about the work of an earlier Egyptian mathematician named Diophantus. Diophantus, known as the "Father of Algebra," worked with quadratic equations and equations having more than one solution. Historians believe that Hypatia's writings provide us with the only surviving copy of his algebra. Some believe that Hypatia deserves to be known as the "Mother of Algebra" because her work preserved and added to that of Diophantus.

Hypatia was also interested in science. In her writings, she described plans for building an instrument called an astrolabe. This device was used to measure the positions of the stars and planets. Hypatia also invented several pieces of apparatus for working with liquids. Among these was a device for distilling water.

Hypatia lived during a time when Egypt was in the process of great social change. When she was still in her prime—in her forties—a mob of fanatics pulled her from her carriage and murdered her because she was true to the old religion. Some historians believe that Hypatia's death in 415 represents the end of ancient mathematics and science. However, her life story continues to inspire students as an example of a woman who excelled in these fields.

Hypatia

Questions for Critical Thinking

1. What factors do you think may have contributed to Alexandria becoming a center of learning?

   _____

   _____

   _____

2. Give some additional applications of the conic sections (circle, ellipse, parabola, hyperbola).

   _____

   _____

   _____

3. Why do you think the importance of the conic sections was not fully recognized until the seventeenth century?

   _____

   _____

   _____

4. Hypatia described an instrument for measuring the positions of the stars and planets. How might such measurements have been used during Hypatia's time?

   _____

   _____

   _____

5. Hypatia's father, Theon, was also a mathematician. Do you think it was common in Hypatia's day for a woman to follow in her father's profession? Why or why not?

   _____

   _____

   _____

Hypatia

Triangular, Square, and Polygonal Numbers

Materials: pencil, circular counters (pennies, bottle caps, beans, or similar objects)

What is the relationship between whole numbers and geometry? Hypatia studied number patterns and their relationship to geometric figures. You can experiment with some of these patterns.

1. Place one counter on the table. Then add two counters to form an equilateral triangle as shown. Then add three counters, again forming an equilateral triangle. Continue the process by adding four, and then five, counters.

   The **triangular numbers** are the number of counters in each equilateral triangle. Fill in the next two numbers in the list below.

   Triangular numbers are: 1, 3, 6, _____ , _____ , ...

2. Start with one counter and then add consecutive odd numbers of counters (3, 5, 7, and so on) so that each addition completes the square as shown. The number of counters in the squares are the **square numbers.**

   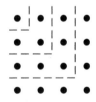

   List the first five square numbers you have formed: _____ , _____ , _____ , _____ , _____

3. By arranging counters into various polygonal shapes, other **polygonal numbers** can be formed. Use patterns from Steps 1 and 2 to complete the following table.

Triangular	1	3	6					36	
Square	1	4	9					64	
Pentagonal	1	5	12	22			70		
Hexagonal	1	6	15	28				120	
Heptagonal	1	7	18	34			112		

4. Describe at least two patterns that you see in the above table.

   _____

   _____

   _____

Hypatia

A Problem with Many Solutions

Materials: pencil, calculator

One of Hypatia's best-known works was her commentary on the mathematics of Diophantus. Diophantus studied problems that led to equations with more than one solution. Such equations are known as **indeterminate equations.** For example, the problem of changing a one-dollar bill into nickels and dimes leads to an indeterminate equation because there are many different solutions to the problem.

In her paper on Diophantus, Hypatia posed the following problem. Find a number that satisfies these two conditions: (1) it is the sum of two squares, and (2) its square is also the sum of two squares.

Many solutions exist. Hypatia studied a whole class of numbers that could be solutions. These numbers are of the form $4n + 1$, where $n = 1, 2, 3$, and so on. Many numbers of this form are solutions to the problem. In particular, the formula $4n + 1$ generates prime numbers that are always the sum of two squares. Are their squares also the sum of two squares? To find out, use your calculator to help you complete the following table. You do not need to complete rows for which $4n + 1$ is not prime.

n	$4n + 1$	Sum of Squares	$(4n + 1)^2$	Sum of Squares
1	5	1 + 4	25	9 + 16
2	9 (not prime)	X	X	X
3	13	4 + 9	169	25 + 144
4				
5				
6				
7				
8				
9				

1. Circle the prime numbers in the second column of the table that are solutions to the above problem.

2. Do you think all prime numbers of the form $4n + 1$ are solutions to the above problem?

_____

The Incas

Records in Knots

The Inca culture was a great civilization with a strong working government. The Incas were indigenous South-American people whose way of life spread to all of their neighbors from about 1400 to 1540. Their civilization included areas of present-day Peru, Bolivia, Ecuador, Chile, and Argentina. When the Incas took control of an area, they left the local culture intact but added their institutions of government. They considered these institutions to be "gifts." If the "gifts" were accepted, there was no use of force. In this way, they gained control of most of the west coast of South America. They called this area *Tawantinsuyu*, meaning "land of the four quarters."

The Incas controlled their vast territory with a strong communication system based on a network of highways. Another form of control came from the orderly, precise records kept on *quipus*. A quipu (pronounced KEE poo) is a collection of cords with knots tied in them as shown in the illustration at the right. The cords were made of dyed cotton or wool, which were abundant materials in the Inca world. Anything that could be counted was recorded on quipus, including the census of each village, the output of gold mines, the composition of the work force, and dates of important historic events.

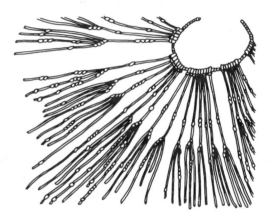

Quipus were probably not invented by the Incas, but the Incas made quipus an essential part of government. Quipu makers were trained at a school in Cuzco, the Inca capital. The illustration at the right shows an Inca community official using a quipu. Quipu makers were a professional class whose full-time job was representing what was going on in the world by logically relating numbers, colors, and positions on a cord.

The knots on a quipu represented numbers of a base-ten system like the base-ten number system you are familiar with. The planning and construction of a quipu involved types of cord connections, relative placement of cords, and color selections. Color coding was used to relate cords and to distinguish them from each other. A large "color vocabulary" was used to create varied patterns expressing relationships between the items being recorded. A quipu such as the one diagrammed at the right might have represented the entire inventory of a major storehouse. Because the fiber cords were detachable, quipus were easily updated, as well as highly portable.

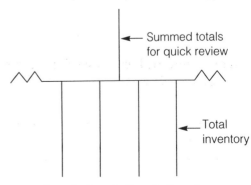

← Summed totals for quick review

← Total inventory

Item 1   Item 2   Item 3   Item 4

The Incas

Records in Knots *(continued)*

Although anything now recorded with paper and pen could also be recorded on a quipu, there are differences in the basic concept underlying each form of record keeping. A piece of paper presents a flat, two-dimensional surface and is filled with information right-to-left and top-to-bottom. As a group of cords, a quipu presents no such surface. The relative position of a cord, its color, and the number and type of knots in it all give it meaning. Creating or reading a quipu involves the ability to think with color in three dimensions. Because the world is a colorful, three-dimensional place, the potential uses of such a record-keeping device seem unlimited.

Questions for Critical Thinking

1. Describe two examples of data in contemporary society that could be recorded on a quipu.

   _____

   _____

2. How do you think a quipu might be used to keep track of your income and expenditures. What categories would you have to include? How could you keep track of these categories?

   _____

   _____

   _____

3. Give three examples of modern systems that use color coding. Describe how the color coding functions.

   _____

   _____

   _____

4. Why might the Incas have chosen to record information on knotted cords rather than by some other method?

   _____

   _____

   _____

The Incas

Making a Quipu

Materials: pencil, three different colors of heavy yarn (2 meters of each color), colored pencils (optional)

The Inca quipu makers had to plan the organization of their quipu before they began tying knots. In this activity, you will practice various ways of organizing data into the quipu format and then design and create your own quipu.

Organizing Quipu Data: Situation 1

Suppose you need to record seven pieces of information: the weight of three bags of freeze-dried potatoes (a staple of the Inca diet) and the outdoor temperature at four different times of the day. First, create tables to organize this data. Then describe a possible quipu format to show this data. Draw a picture of the quipu format. Indicate how you would use color if you need it.

Organizing Quipu Data: Situation 2

Suppose you are in charge of Inca textile storehouses in two areas. Each area has four storehouses. You need to record the number of brown, white, and red blankets in each storehouse. First devise tables to organize this data. Then describe a possible quipu format to show this data. Draw a picture of the quipu format. Indicate how you would use color if you need it.

The Incas

Making a Quipu *(continued)*

1. Now choose a set of data that is of interest to you. Organize your data into a table in the space below.

2. In the space below, make a drawing showing how you plan to arrange your quipu. Indicate the use of color if you need it.

3. Select the main cord for your quipu. Prepare the cords that will be attached. These are the main units of your quipu. Each of these cords is two-ply, with one end forming an open loop and the other finished with a small knot. Assemble your quipu as shown below.

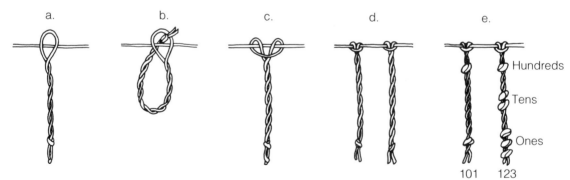

   a. Take the looped end of the cord and pry it open. Place the open loop beneath the main cord at the point where you wish to attach it.
   b. Pass the knotted end of the cord over the main cord and through the loop.
   c. Pull the knotted end of the cord until the loop is tight around the main cord.
   d. Attach as many cords as necessary to the main cord.
   e. Begin tying knots to represent your data. Remember that the knots represent base-ten numbers.

Harvey Itano

Sickle-Cell Researcher

D r. Harvey Itano, a Japanese-American physician, university professor, and medical researcher, is well known for his studies of the disease known as sickle-cell anemia. *Anemia* is a general name for a condition in which a person does not have enough functioning red blood cells. The function of a red blood cell is to carry oxygen throughout the body. Without enough functioning red blood cells, the body becomes oxygen-deprived. Sickle-cell anemia is a hereditary form of anemia affecting people with African ancestry. One of every five-hundred African Americans in the United States inherits this condition.

People with sickle-cell anemia (SCA) have red blood cells that contain a different form of the oxygen-carrying protein, hemoglobin. Hemoglobin is a complex protein made up of two pairs of small proteins. Each of the small proteins is a folded chain of many amino acids with a "heme" group containing a single iron atom in its center. In one pair of the smaller proteins, a single amino acid differs in people with SCA. The change in the hemoglobin is shown in the illustration at the right.

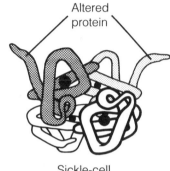 

Altered protein   Normal protein

Sickle-cell hemoglobin HbS

Normal hemoglobin HbA

This small difference is enough to make the hemoglobin molecules stick together and link to each other instead of linking to oxygen molecules. The red blood cells then "sickle" as shown in the illustration at the right. The changed shape of the cells can cause blocked blood vessels, one of the symptoms of sickle-cell anemia.

"Sickled" red blood cells

"Normal" red blood cells

Dr. Itano conducted many detailed studies on hemoglobin structure while working with Nobel Laureate Linus Pauling at the California Institute of Technology. He discovered and characterized many unusual forms of hemoglobin, including the forms called Hemoglobin C, Hemoglobin D, and Hemoglobin E. The hemoglobin that causes SCA is known as Hemoglobin S (HbS). Normal hemoglobin is known as Hemoglobin A (HbA). Dr. Itano also studied a another hereditary form of anemia, known as *thalassemia*, which occurs in people with Mediterranean and Southeast-Asian ancestry.

In 1949, Dr. Itano made some interesting discoveries using the technique of *gel electrophoresis*. This technique separates proteins using an electric charge. The proteins travel different distances across the gel depending on their size and their amino acid make-up.

Harvey Itano

Sickle-Cell Researcher *(continued)*

The illustration at the right shows the results of Dr. Itano's gel electrophoresis experiment. He analyzed hemoglobin from a person with SCA, a well person thought to carry the SCA gene, and a normal control. This data shows that the well person thought to carry the SCA gene has both Hemoglobin A and Hemoglobin S. For this and other work, Dr. Itano received the first Martin Luther King Jr. Medical Achievement Award.

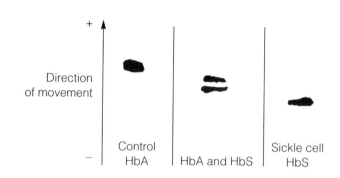

Harvey Akio Itano was born in Sacramento, California, of Japanese parents in 1920. He graduated with Highest Honors in Chemistry from the University of California, Berkeley, in 1942. Despite his high honors, he was not allowed to receive his diploma in person. During World War II, the United States government forcibly removed 120,000 Japanese Americans from their homes and sent them to internment camps in remote areas. Harvey Itano was sent to an internment camp at Tule Lake, California.

After the war, Harvey Itano left California and attended St. Louis University Medical School. He returned to California after medical school and began his hemoglobin work as a Ph.D. project with Dr. Linus Pauling. After receiving his doctorate, he spent the next twenty years doing research at the National Institutes of Health. In 1970, Dr. Itano became Professor of Pathology in the medical school at the University of California, San Diego, where he now holds the post of Professor Emeritus.

Questions for Critical Thinking

1. If a person has anemia, his or her blood cells are oxygen-deprived. Describe how you think a person with anemia might feel.

   _____

2. What are some possible causes of anemia, other than sickle-cell disease?

   _____

   _____

3. The amino acid difference in the hemoglobin of people with SCA was originally caused by a genetic mutation. Generally, mutations that are harmful are eliminated over many generations. Why might this mutation have survived?

   _____

   _____

Name _____   Date _____

Patterns of Inheritance

Materials: pencil, extra sheet of paper

Sickle-cell anemia is known to be a hereditary disease. It has a pattern of inheritance that closely follows the model for recessive traits described by early geneticist Gregor Mendel. For a recessive trait to appear, a person must have inherited two copes of the recessive gene. This is called being *homozygous* for the recessive gene. People who have sickle-cell anemia are homozygous for the gene for the altered hemoglobin HbS.

If a person has one copy of the HbS gene and one gene for normal hemoglobin HbA, they are *heterozygous* for the recessive gene. Although people who are heterozygous for the sickle-cell gene are generally not ill, they can pass the gene on to their offspring. In this activity, you will look at two cases and use a technique of genetic analysis, called a Punnet Square, to analyze the odds of inheriting a genetic disease such as sickle-cell anemia.

Consider a case in which one parent does not carry any genes for sickle-cell hemoglobin HbS. This parent can be represented by the letters *AA*. The other parent has one gene for normal hemoglobin HbA and one gene for HbS. This parent can be represented by the letters *AS*. Each of these parents produces sex cells (eggs or sperm) containing one gene. The diagram at the right shows the possibilities.

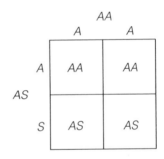

1. What are the chances of this couple having a child with sickle-cell anemia?

_____

2. What are the chances of this couple having a child who is heterozygous for the sickle-cell gene?

_____

Now, analyze a case in which both parents are heterozygous for the sickle-cell gene. Create your own Punnet Square on a separate sheet of paper and represent each parent with the letters *AS*. Then answer the following questions.

3. What are the chances of this couple having a child with sickle-cell anemia?

_____

4. What are the chances of this couple having a child who is heterozygous for the sickle-cell gene?

_____

Harvey Itano

Deadly Disease or Life-Saving Trait?

Materials: pencil, world map

Study the maps below and compare them to a map of the world. Use the information to answer the questions below.

Distribution of Sickle Cell Anemia

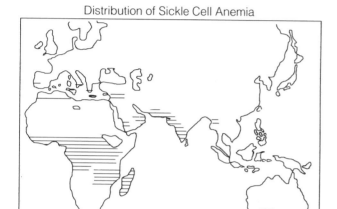

Distribution of Malaria Parasite

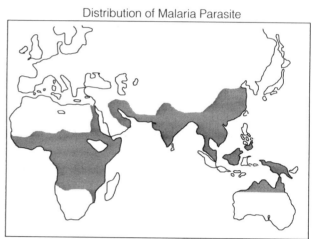

1. What is shown on the map on the left? What countries are affected?

   _____

   _____

2. What is shown on the map on the right? What countries are affected?

   _____

   _____

3. What countries are affected by both conditions?

   _____

   _____

4. Give a possible explanation of why these two conditions occur together.

   _____

   _____

   _____

Ernest Just

Goo, Goop, and Ooze: the Secrets of Life?

The subtitle on this page could have been a newspaper headline describing the research of African-American biologist **Ernest Just** (1883–1941). The slimy ooze sensationalized in popular films of today is modeled after the subject of his research—the cytoplasm found in living cells. A cell's cytoplasm is made up of a jellylike fluid that contains salts, water, organic molecules, and the cell's organelles ("little organs"). It was this seemingly static ooze that captured the analytical mind of Dr. Just. He hypothesized that it had an important function, even though many scientists of his day thought it was just a filler material. The diagram at the right shows the parts of an animal cell.

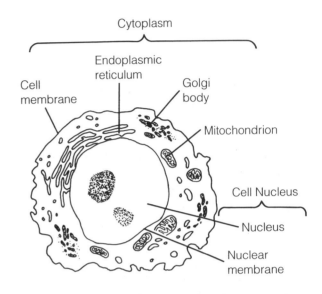

Dr. Just focused his laboratory research on exploring the cytoplasm's function in the cell. After many years of study, he found evidence that the outer boundary of the cytoplasm, including the cell membrane, has important functions. One of these functions is the control of homeostasis, the biological balance between the cell and the external environment.

Modern molecular biology has offered further evidence that Dr. Just was correct. The cell membrane, illustrated at the right, has been shown to be a complex mosaic of lipids and proteins. The many different proteins in the membrane allow it to actively interface with the environment. The cytoplasm within the membrane is now known to be a complex, constantly-streaming mix of fluid and proteins where most life processes take place. A network of protein filaments, known as the cytoskeleton, helps the cell keep its shape and transport materials internally.

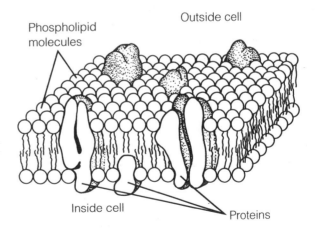

Dr. Just also observed that the cell membrane plays an important role in the process of fertilization (the union of sperm and egg cells). He worked with egg and sperm cells from the spiky creature known as the sea urchin. Dr. Just observed that some sea urchin egg cells treated with plain seawater began to develop in a way similar to fertilized eggs. This process, known as artificial parthenogenesis, proves that the egg itself contains the "program" for development. Dr Just's experiments showed that the process is triggered by the cell membrane.

Multiculturalism in Mathematics, Science, and Technology

Ernest Just

Goo, Goop, and Ooze: the Secrets of Life? *(continued)*

The study of parthenogenesis launched Dr. Just's lifelong research into the embryology of the sea urchin. While Professor of Biology at Howard University, he spent every summer during the years 1909 to 1930 studying sea urchins at the Marine Biological Laboratory in Woods Hole, Massachusetts. His work helped make the development of the sea urchin one of the best-understood processes in embryology. The multistep process by which a single cell develops into a free swimming larva takes 48 hours and can be observed with a simple microscope. Dr. Just spent many painstaking hours observing and recording the process. The larval form of the sea urchin and the spiky adult are shown at the right.

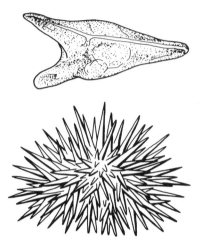

In addition to his laboratory work, Dr. Just was an important figure in black education. He served as head of the Departments of Biology and Physiology at Howard University and was a prominent faculty member in the School of Medicine there. He pointed out to his students that understanding cell function was crucial to the understanding and treatment of many diseases.

Dr. Just also showed his students that life's obstacles could be overcome in pursuit of an educational goal. After his father's death, Just had to do farm work throughout his grade school and high school years to help his family. He left home after high school and worked to support himself during four additional years of college preparatory studies. He then entered Dartmouth College. There, he met eminent biologist William Patten, who urged him to specialize in cell biology. While still in college, Just began the work that later brought him worldwide fame and honors.

Throughout his career, Dr. Just produced over seventy research papers and three internationally known books on fertilization and experimental embryology. His work is still highly respected today and correlates well with recent findings about the molecular nature of cytoplasm and the cell membrane.

Questions for Critical Thinking

1. Why do you think Ernest Just chose to study cytoplasm when many other scientists were convinced it had no function?

_____

_____

_____

Ernest Just

Questions for Critical Thinking *(continued)*

2. Study the sketch of the cell membrane on the first page of this unit. How do you think it controls materials going in and out of the cell?

_____

_____

_____

_____

3. Why might the study of cell function be important in finding new disease treatments?

_____

_____

_____

_____

4. In some organisms, such as bees and ants, parthenogenesis occurs naturally. Give some possible explanations of why this might occur.

_____

_____

_____

_____

5. Give a possible explanation of why the larval and adult forms of the sea urchin are so strikingly different. Then name some other organisms in which the larval and adult stages are very different.

_____

_____

_____

_____

Ernest Just

Which Came First? — Embryology of the Sea Urchin

Materials: pencil

Dr. Ernest Just spent many hours in the laboratory observing the changes that take place as a sea urchin egg develops into a larva. Shown below are some of the stages of development that he saw through his microscope.

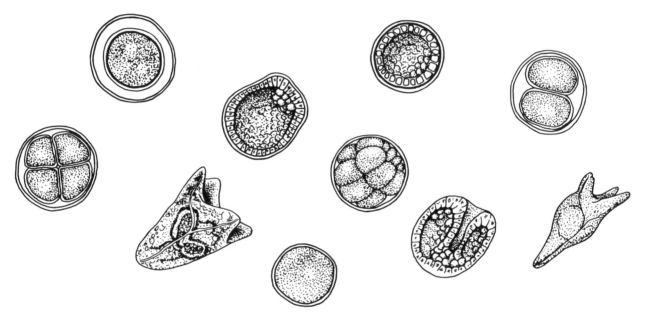

1. Can you determine the sequence of events? Study the drawings and use the boxes below to redraw the events in the order in which you think they occur.

2. In your own words, describe the step-by-step process that you have just drawn.

_____

_____

Ernest Just

The Cell Membrane—Master Regulator

Materials: cucumber slices, salt, water, beaker or jar, paper towels, laboratory balance

The cell membrane is a very thin layer of the outer cytoplasm. It is only about ten nanometers (10^{-9} meters) thick. Although it is difficult to see in a light microscope, Dr. Ernest Just spent many hours observing the configuration and response of the cell membrane in both plant and animal cells. Dr. Just found evidence that the cell membrane controls what goes in and out of the cell. It is now known that the cell membrane is *selectively permeable*. This means that the membrane allows only certain substances to enter and leave the cell.

Plants such as the cucumber contain a great deal of water in their cells. The water is contained within the cell membrane, which lies next to an elastic cell wall. Water in the cell exerts turgor pressure against the cell wall and keeps the plant rigid. When plants wilt, it is because the cells do not contain enough water to exert pressure against the cell walls and keep the plant upright.

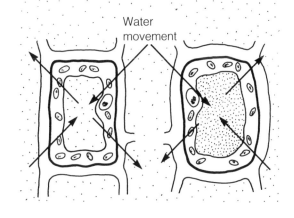

1. Compare the two plant cells shown here. In which of the two plant cells is there more turgor pressure? Explain.

_____

_____

Water is one of the substances to which cell membranes are permeable. In the following activity, you will experiment with conditions that cause water to move in and out of cucumber cells. This process is called *osmosis*. Osmosis is defined as the movement of water across a membrane from a region of greater water concentration to a region of lesser water concentration. Keep this in mind as you experiment with the cucumber slices.

2. Using a laboratory balance, find the mass of each of two cucumber slices. Record the masses in the left columns of the tables below.

Slice 1

Mass When Fresh	Mass After Salt Treatment (20 min.)

Slice 2

Mass When Fresh	Mass After Water Treatment (20 min.)

Ernest Just

The Cell Membrane—Master Regulator *(continued)*

Place Slice 1 on a paper towel with enough salt to cover it completely. Let it sit undisturbed for 20 minutes. Place Slice 2 in a beaker or jar, cover it with water, and let it sit undisturbed for 20 minutes.

3. While waiting, observe the characteristics of another fresh cucumber slice. Record your observations.

   _____

   _____

   _____

4. After 20 minutes have elapsed, clean off the salt-treated cucumber slice and measure its mass again. Record the mass in the appropriate table on the previous page. Measure the mass of the water-treated cucumber slice and record it in the table. Explain any changes in mass that you observed.

   _____

   _____

   _____

5. Compare the characteristics of the salt-treated cucumber slice to those of the fresh slice that you observed in Step 3. How are they the same? How are they different?

   _____

   _____

6. Compare the characteristics of the water-treated cucumber slice to those of the fresh slice that you observed in Step 3. How are they the same? How are they different?

   _____

   _____

7. Explain the results of your experiment in terms of the process of osmosis.

   _____

   _____

   _____

Omar Khayyam

The Proof of Truth

I n Europe and the Western Hemisphere, **Omar Khayyam** (ca. 1050–1122) is famous mainly as a romantic poet. In his native Iran and the neighboring Soviet Union, he is regarded as a great mathematician and scientist. In fact, in these regions, he is called "The Proof of Truth," the highest praise for a scientist.

As a young man living in Persia, Khayyam (ky YHAM) made good progress in his study of science. His family was not wealthy, so he had to make his own way in the world. *Khayyam* means tent maker—an honorable trade, but not usually the road to riches. However, Omar was lucky. Eleventh-century Islamic rulers encouraged the study of science and mathematics at a time when these fields were at a low ebb in Europe. Universities flourished in the Islamic world and many observatories were built.

By the time he was 17, it was said that Khayyam had a profound knowledge of every subject of study. However, he was forced to flee his home, perhaps because his ideas were considered offensive. After he left his native city of Nishapur, Khayyam went to Samarkand, now in Uzbekistan, U.S.S.R. Some of the famous architecture of Samarkand is illustrated at the right.

In Samarkand, a powerful friend got Omar a good job at the court. His only duty was to make astrological predictions for the Shah of Samarkand. Since Khayyam was an astronomer who did not believe in astrology, he only pretended to do astrology because that gave him access to an excellent observatory at Isfahan. Also, it kept him on good terms with the Shah.

In addition to his work in astronomy, Khayyam did much original work in algebra and geometry. In algebra, Khayyam studied quadratic and third-degree equations and described general methods for solving them. Much of Khayyam's work in geometry centered around Euclid's fifth postulate.

A postulate is a mathematical statement that is accepted as true without proof. Euclid's fifth postulate states that given a line ℓ and a point P not on ℓ, there is only one line that contains P and is parallel to ℓ. Although the geometry of Euclid was admired by Islamic mathematicians, they thought it was not perfect. They tried to show that Euclid's fifth postulate could actually be proven from his first four postulates.

Omar Khayyam

The Proof of Truth *(continued)*

Neither Omar Khayyam nor his fellow mathematicians succeeded in proving the fifth postulate. But their "thought experiments" were used hundreds of years later in Italy by Girolamo Saccheri who developed the groundwork of what is now known as non-Euclidean geometry.

Questions for Critical Thinking

1. In Omar Khayyam's time, why was it common for mathematicians to also work in other sciences?

   _____

   _____

   _____

2. What are some similarities and differences between astronomy and astrology?

   _____

   _____

   _____

3. A postulate is a statement that is accepted as true without proof. Give an example of a postulate other than Euclid's fifth postulate.

   _____

   _____

   _____

4. A sample of Omar Khayyam's writing appears below.

   > From this globe of black clay to the height of Saturn,
   > I have solved all the major problems.
   > I have opened difficult knots with cunning.
   > Every knot has been opened except the knot of death.

   What can you say about Khayyam based on this poem?

   _____

   _____

Omar Khayyam

A Look at Euclid's Fifth Postulate

Materials: pencil, two sheets of quarter-inch graph paper, straightedge, scissors, beach
ball (or other ball, at least 8 inches in diameter), transparent tape

Euclid's fifth postulate states that given a line ℓ
and a point P not on ℓ, there is only one line that
contains P and is parallel to ℓ. Omar Khayyam
and his contemporaries studied this postulate
and tried to prove it using Euclid's first four
postulates. In fact, mathematicians tried to prove
this postulate for many hundreds of years,
dating from the time of Euclid, around 300 B.C.

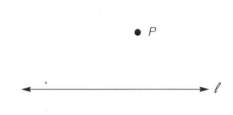

It is now known that Euclid's fifth postulate is independent of the first four postulates and
cannot be proven from them. However, the attempts to prove Euclid's fifth postulate laid
the foundation for other systems of geometry, known as non-Euclidean geometry.

The familiar Euclidean geometry describes "flat" space very well. The fifth postulate is the
basis for many familiar properties of parallel lines, right triangles, rectangles, and other
figures. Although the surface of the earth is actually curved, any small region on the earth
is approximately flat and the fifth postulate seems quite natural. If you can imagine a
universe in which space itself is curved, the situation would be somewhat different.

The two theorems stated below are equivalent to the fifth postulate. You can test these
theorems on the curved surface of a ball—a "universe" with curved space—to see how
well the fifth postulate works in such a setting.

Two Theorems Equivalent to the Fifth Postulate

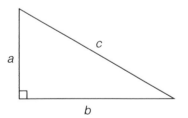

Pythagorean Theorem: $c^2 = a^2 + b^2$

If $\angle G$ and $\angle F$ are right angles, and
$\overline{DG} \cong \overline{EF}$, then $DEFG$ is a rectangle.

1.   On a sheet of graph paper, use a straightedge to draw a right triangle with legs of
     length 3 inches and 4 inches. According to the Pythagorean Theorem, what should the
     length of the hypotenuse be?

_____

Verify this by cutting out a long, thin strip of the graph paper and using it to measure
the hypotenuse.

Multiculturalism in Mathematics, Science, and Technology

Omar Khayyam

A Look at Euclid's Fifth Postulate *(continued)*

2. On another sheet of graph paper, use your straight-edge to draw three sides of a quadrilateral so that the base angles are right angles and the opposite sides are congruent. With a straightedge, draw a dotted line to connect points D and E. What can you say about the segments $\overline{DE}$ and $\overline{GF}$?

_____

What type of figure is quadrilateral *DEFG*?

_____

3. Use scissors to cut out the legs of the right triangle. You should have a very narrow, L-shaped piece of paper. Similarly, cut out the base and congruent sides of the quadrilateral. Do not include the top side.

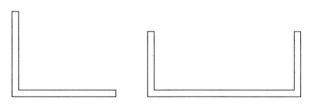

4. Carefully tape the right angle on the surface of a ball. With the strip of graph paper, measure the new hypotenuse. Is it 5 inches?

_____

5. Carefully tape the base and sides of the quadrilateral on the surface of the ball. With the strip of graph paper, measure the distance across the open side of the quadrilateral. Is it equal to the length of the base?

_____

On the surface of the ball, is the quadrilateral a rectangle?

_____

6. Do the two theorems stated on the previous page work on a curved surface?

_____

7. What does this tell you about Euclid's fifth postulate?

_____

_____

Sonya Kovalevsky

Saturn, Symmetry, and Solutions

Although **Sonya Kovalevsky** (1850–1891) was the daughter of a Russian nobleman, her great achievements in science and mathematics were earned through hard work, determination, and sacrifice. As a girl, Kovalevsky taught herself trigonometry from a book written by a neighbor. At the age of fourteen, she often visited a room of her home where pages from her father's calculus textbook served as a temporary wall covering. By studying the pages, Kovalevsky learned calculus. Later, when Kovalevsky formally studied calculus, her tremendous potential was immediately recognized by her tutor.

Despite Kovalevsky's ability and determination, life for women in nineteenth-century Russia was not easy. Kovalevsky could not travel freely, could not attend public lectures, and had difficulty finding a job. At the age of eighteen, she left Russia to study at the universities in Heidelberg and Berlin. Although women were not allowed to attend university lectures, Kovalevsky was tutored by several renowned mathematicians. She received her doctorate from the University of Göttingen in 1874.

Kovalevsky went on to write remarkable research papers on partial differential equations, Abelian integrals, and infinite series. Her name is also associated with the Cauchy-Kovalevsky Theorem of partial differential equations. The theorem discusses whether a solution exists to certain types of equations. It also discusses whether a solution is the only possible one.

Later in her career, Kovalevsky worked with the famous mathematician Karl Weierstrass and received a life professorship in mathematics at the University of Stockholm. In 1888, Kovalevsky won the *Prix Bordin* from the French Academy of Sciences. Her winning paper, "On the Rotation of a Solid Body About a Fixed Point," so impressed the judges that they increased the prize money from 3000 to 5000 francs.

In addition to her work in mathematics, Kovalevsky made important contributions to astronomy. In one of her papers, she concluded that the rings of Saturn were egg-shaped ovals with one line of symmetry rather than ellipses with two lines of symmetry. Her mathematical approach to this subject was considered a model for other scientists.

In 1891, at the age of 41, Sonya Kovalevsky died of pneumonia. At the time of her death, Kovalevsky was at the peak of her career and the height of her fame. She is still regarded by historians and mathematicians as one of the greatest mathematical talents of the nineteenth century.

Sonya Kovalevsky

Questions for Critical Thinking

1. Describe some of the obstacles that Sonya Kovalevsky had to overcome to become one of the greatest mathematicians of her time.

2. Kovalevsky wrote about the existence and uniqueness of solutions to certain types of equations. In your own words, explain what is meant by "existence and uniqueness."

3. Kovalevsky concluded that Saturn's rings are egg-shaped rather than elliptical. What else do you know about Saturn's rings?

4. In addition to her fame as a mathematician, Kovalevsky was also well known as a writer of novels and dramas. Her works include *The University Lecturer*, *The Woman Nihilist*, and *The Struggle for Happiness*. Do you think it is unusual or unlikely for a mathematician to also be a writer of fiction? Why or why not?

Name _____ Date _____

A Look at Symmetry

Materials: pencil, straightedge, small rectangular mirror (optional)

Sonya Kovalevsky concluded that Saturn's rings are egg-shaped, with one line (or axis) of symmetry. A *line of symmetry* is a line that cuts a figure into two identical halves; if the figure were folded along the line, the two halves would match exactly. The two halves can also be thought of as "mirror images" of each other. The figures at the right illustrate lines of symmetry for an egg shape and an ellipse.

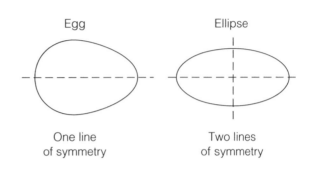

1. Use a straightedge to draw all lines of symmetry for each of the following figures. You may wish to test your lines of symmetry with a small rectangular mirror.

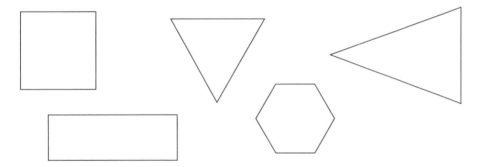

2. Consider the capital letters of the alphabet shown below.

A B C D E F G H I J K L M N O P Q R S T U V W X Y Z

Which letters have a vertical axis of symmetry?

_____

Which letters have a horizontal axis of symmetry?

_____

Which letters have both a horizontal and vertical axis of symmetry?

_____

3. Name a figure that has an infinite number of lines of symmetry.

_____

Sonya Kovalevsky

Infinite Sequences

Materials: pencil

In the nineteenth century, Sonya Kovalevsky and her colleagues studied the behavior of infinite sequences. Record the next three numbers in each sequence below. Then describe each sequence in the space provided.

1. 1, 2, 4, 8, 16, 32, _____ , _____ , _____ , …

_____

2. 1, 3, 6, 10, 15, 21, _____ , _____ , _____ , …

_____

3. 4, 11, 18, 25, 32, 39, _____ , _____ , _____ , …

_____

4. 2, 3, 5, 7, 11, 13, 17, _____ , _____ , _____ , …

_____

5. –1, 0, 1, 0, –1, 0, 1, _____ , _____ , _____ , …

_____

Use your work with the above sequences to answer Questions 6 and 7.

6. A sequence in which a constant d can be added to each term to get the next term is called an **arithmetic sequence.** The constant d is called the **common difference.** Which of the above sequences is an arithmetic sequence? What is the common difference?

_____

7. A sequence in which each term can be multiplied by a constant r to get the next term is called a **geometric sequence.** The constant r is called the **common ratio.** Which of the above sequences is a geometric sequence? What is the common ratio?

_____

8. Make up an infinite sequence of your own. Write the first six terms in the space below. Then exchange papers with a partner and see if you can find the next three numbers in your partner's sequence.

_____

Lewis Howard Latimer

Latimer's Light

The most important invention of African-American engineer **Lewis Howard Latimer** (1848–1928) may be his development of the first practical electric light bulb. He developed the process used for manufacturing carbon filaments for the Thomas A. Edison light bulb. The filament—the very fine, threadlike material in a light bulb—glows whenever electricity passes through it. Latimer's work on the filament was a major technological advancement. It was his work that made electric light bulbs safe and inexpensive for ordinary households.

Here is how Latimer's light bulb works. The carbon filament is a very dense and hard material similar to coal (a form of carbon). The filament is connected to highly conductive wires made of copper or platinum. Electric current passes easily through the wires but encounters resistance when it reaches the filament, which is a poor conductor. This process makes the filament so hot that it produces white heat, known as *incandescence*. The hotter the filament becomes, the brighter the light that is produced.

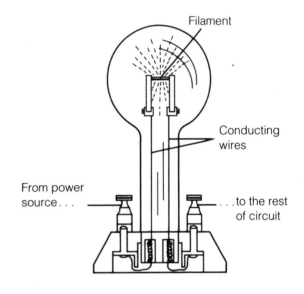

Latimer solved the problem of how to keep the filament from immediately burning itself out. He did this by removing all traces of oxygen from the bulb. In the absence of oxygen, no combustion can occur.

Latimer had many other technological and scientific achievements. He wrote the first book on electric lighting. It was entitled *Incandescent Electric Lighting: A Practical Description of the Edison System* and was published in 1890. This book served as a guide for lighting engineers throughout the world. In addition to his patent for the light bulb filament, Latimer's patents included a toilet for railroad cars, an improved electric lamp, and the threads for the electric light bulb socket. He was instrumental in bringing electric lighting to office buildings, homes, subway stations, and railroad cars in New York and other major cities.

Latimer's many achievements came despite early hardships. Latimer's parents escaped slavery by fleeing the state of Virginia. Abolitionists in Massachusetts helped them purchase their freedom and Lewis Latimer was born as a free person of color in Chelsea, Massachusetts. Even as a young boy, in elementary school, he was quite curious and industrious. He worked in his father's barbershop and helped with odd jobs after school. When Latimer was ten, his father deserted the family. His mother found work as a ship's stewardess and separated the four children, sending them to live on farm schools or with relatives. By chance, Lewis met his brother again and the two young men ran away together to Boston. Once there, they went to work to help reunite their family.

Lewis Howard Latimer

Latimer's Light (*continued*)

At the age of thirteen, Lewis sold copies of the newspaper, *The Liberator*. When he was only fifteen years old, he enlisted in the Navy during the Civil War. After receiving an honorable discharge, Latimer was eventually hired as an office assistant by the firm of Crosby and Gould, Patent Solicitors. He bought used drawing books and second-hand drawing instruments. By day, he observed the draftsmen; by night, he practiced drawing. Soon his quiet efforts paid off. He was promoted to junior draftsman and had the responsibility of making models and drawing plans of inventions. From Latimer's work as a draftsman, he became interested in developing and patenting his own inventions.

Hiram Maxim, Chief Engineer of the United States Electrical Lighting Company, soon offered Latimer a job as draftsman and secretary. When Maxim's firm moved to New York City, Latimer was assigned the task of improving the incandescent lamp. In 1882, Latimer received his own patent for the improved carbon filament. Latimer later became Chief Electrical Engineer for the firm and directed the installation of electric lighting for the streets of New York City, Philadelphia, Montreal, and London.

In the 1920's, Latimer joined a group of renowned inventors called the Edison Pioneers. The scientists in this group were all colleagues of Thomas A. Edison. When Latimer, the only African-American member of the Edison Pioneers, died in 1928, his peers drafted a eulogy. It praised Latimer for his broadmindedness, his versatility, and his intellect. It concluded, "Mr. Latimer was a full member—an esteemed member—of the Edison Pioneers."

Questions for Critical Thinking

1. An electric current produces effects that are thermal, chemical, and magnetic. Latimer used an electric current to make his incandescent lamp work. Was he most concerned with producing thermal, chemical, or magnetic effects? Explain.

   _____

   _____

2. Oxygen is necessary for burning, but there is no oxygen inside a light bulb. What do you think really happens when a light bulb "burns out"?

   _____

   _____

3. Suppose you had two light bulbs that were identical in every way except that one had a thicker filament than the other. What would you expect to happen?

   _____

   _____

Lewis Howard Latimer

Electric Experiences

Materials: pencil, aluminum foil, 6-volt lantern battery, two tablespoons of salt, small saucer, $\frac{1}{4}$ cup of distilled water or tap water, two flashlight bulbs, paper clip, large nail

Lewis Latimer performed many experiments with electricity. At the Edison Company, workers were encouraged to use a team approach to problem solving. Below, you will find some situations that Latimer might have investigated. Try each of them with a partner or group.

1. Sketch a picture of one of your flashlight bulbs in the space at the right. Label the wire and the filament. Which parts of your bulb do you associate with Latimer's investigations? Explain.

_____

_____

2. Cut out a strip of aluminum foil about one foot long and about one-half inch wide. Fold this strip in half lengthwise to strengthen it. Connect one end of the folded foil strip to the negative pole of your battery. Tightly wrap the other end of the folded foil strip around the threads of your bulb. Be sure the foil is not touching the metal on the bottom of the bulb. Carefully form an electric circuit by holding the bulb so that the bottom part of the bulb touches the positive pole of your battery. What happens? Explain what is happening in your own words.

_____

_____

_____

3. Investigate what happens if you rearrange the parts of the circuit. This time, place the bulb near the middle of the foil strip and connect the loose end to the positive battery pole. Explain what happens.

_____

_____

_____

Lewis Howard Latimer

Electric Experiences *(continued)*

4. Investigate what happens when you add a second bulb to your circuit. Wrap the threads of the second bulb with the end of the foil strip near the positive pole. What happens when you press the metal part of this second light bulb against the positive pole of the battery? Are the light bulbs equally bright? Do the two bulbs produce more or less light than the single bulb did? Explain.

_____

_____

_____

5. Pour two tablespoons of salt into the saucer. Add water to just below the rim. Cut out a strip of aluminum foil about one foot long and about one-half inch wide. Fold this strip in half lengthwise to strengthen it. Cut this folded strip into two shorter strips. Connect one of the foil strips to the negative pole of your battery. Connect the other foil strip to the positive pole. Hold the battery so that the two strips of foil are in the water. Do not let the strips touch each other. Carefully observe what is happening and record your observations in the space below. This is an example of a chemical effect produced by electricity.

_____

_____

_____

6. Cut out a strip of aluminum foil about three feet long and about two inches wide. Strengthen this strip by folding it lengthwise three times. Wrap the folded foil strip around the nail in coils, leaving about eight inches of foil free on each end. Connect each end of the foil strip to one of the poles on the battery. Touch the nail to the paper clip. What happens? Explain.

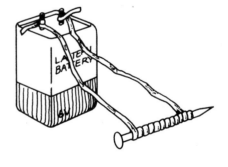

_____

_____

_____

Jan Matzeliger

Shoes that "Last"

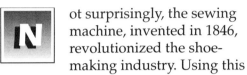

Not surprisingly, the sewing machine, invented in 1846, revolutionized the shoe-making industry. Using this machine, various parts of the shoe could be sewn together quickly and easily. However, no one had been able to invent a machine that could *last* a shoe, that is, attach the upper, leather portion of the shoe to the sole. Many had tried to invent such a device, but it was the African-American inventor **Jan Matzeliger** (1852–1889) who first constructed and patented a machine to last shoes.

Jan Matzeliger was born in Paramaribo, Surinam, on the northern coast of South America, in 1852. When he was ten years old, he began to work with his father at the government machine works. At the age of nineteen, Matzeliger immigrated to the United States where he settled in Philadelphia and worked as a cobbler.

In 1877, Matzeliger moved to Lynn, Massachusetts, which was a major center of the shoemaking industry. He found a job operating a stitching machine. Through this and later jobs, Matzeliger was able to learn much about the trade. He bought books, tools, and drawing instruments and invented several useful devices. By the fall of 1880, Matzeliger had created a prototype for his most important invention—the shoe-lasting machine.

Although he was offered $1500 for the rights to the machine, Matzeliger declined the offer. Instead, he found two wealthy investors, each of whom purchased one third of the rights to the machine. The three formed the Hand Method Lasting Machine Company. This enabled Matzeliger to get a patent for his lasting machine on March 20, 1883. It was the start of a flurry of activity by investors, profit seekers, and others in the shoe industry. Soon the Consolidated Hand Method Lasting Company was formed, with Matzeliger gaining a large block of the stock for his valuable patent. Lynn, Massachusetts, became known as the "shoe capital" of the world.

The shoemaking industry would never be the same. By hand, about 50 shoes could be lasted in one day. With Matzeliger's new machine, nearly 700 shoes could be lasted in the same period. The entire process of positioning the leather, driving the nails, and releasing the completed shoe was done automatically and in less than one minute per shoe.

Jan Matzeliger died of tuberculosis in 1889. After his death, he was awarded several honors. A statue was erected to Matzeliger in the town of Lynn and in 1901 his invention won a gold medal at the Pan-American Exposition. Today, machinery modeled after Matzeliger's invention is still in use.

Jan Matzeliger

Questions for Critical Thinking

1. After the invention of the sewing machine, why do you think it took almost forty years for someone to invent a shoe-lasting machine?

_____

_____

_____

_____

_____

2. At first, Matzeliger's invention was unpopular with some members of the shoemaking industry. Why do you think this was the case?

_____

_____

_____

_____

_____

3. What impact do you think Matzeliger's shoe-lasting machine had for the average person? Explain.

_____

_____

_____

_____

_____

4. As recently as two hundred years ago, shoes were made to be worn on either foot. Give some advantages and disadvantages of this.

_____

_____

_____

_____

Name _____ Date _____

Jan Matzeliger

Shoe Preferences and Data Analysis

Materials: pencil

Jan Matzeliger's shoe-lasting machine revolutionized the shoemaking industry. The machine made it possible to manufacture shoes quickly and efficiently, and, as a result, shoes became more affordable for the average person. It soon became important for shoe designers—called *line builders*— to find out what consumers wanted in a shoe. In the following activity, you will work with a partner to collect and analyze this type of data.

1. The table below lists some factors that line builders say are important in shoe purchases. Rank each of these factors from 1 to 10. Place a "1" in the "Your Ranking" column next to the factor that is most important to you, place a "2" in the "Your Ranking" column next to the factor that is the next most important, and so on. Continue the process until you have placed a 10 next to the factor that you feel is least important.

Factor	Your Ranking (x)	Your Partner's Ranking (y)
Fit		
Brand Name		
Color		
Material		
Durability		
Style		
Price		
Comfort		
Place Manufactured		
Weight		

2. Record your partner's rankings of the ten factors in the appropriate column.

3. Overall, do you and your partner tend to agree or disagree about the importance of the factors? Justify your answer.

_____

_____

Jan Matzeliger

Shoe Preferences and Data Analysis *(continued)*

In the remainder of this activity you will analyze the data in your table and learn one way of answering the question, "Do you and your partner tend to agree or disagree?"

4. Use the grid provided at the right to plot the ten points from your table. The numbers from the "Your Ranking" column should be used as the *x*-coordinates; the numbers from the "Your Partner's Ranking" column should be used as the *y*-coordinates. This type of graph is called a **scatterplot**.

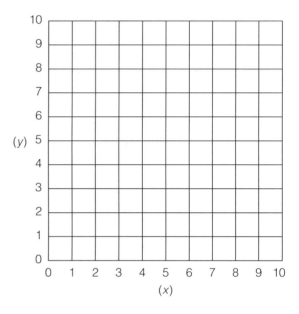

5. Consider the line passing through the points (1, 1) and (10, 10). What is the significance of this line in terms of general agreement or disagreement with your partner?

_____

_____

6. Consider the line passing through the points (1, 10) and (10, 1). What is the significance of this line in terms of general agreement or disagreement with your partner?

_____

_____

7. Now interpret your scatterplot. Are the majority of points in your scatterplot fairly close to either of these lines? What can you say about the general level of agreement or disagreement between you and your partner?

_____

_____

_____

_____

The Maya

The Early Days of Zero

 ne of the most basic ideas in mathematics is the concept of zero. As a place holder, a zero symbol allows you to distinguish between 12 and 102. Although it may be difficult to imagine writing numbers without a symbol for zero, this is how numbers were written for many centuries. Perhaps the earliest known use of a zero place holder was by the Maya.

The Maya flourished from about A.D. 300 to 800 around the region of the Yucatan Peninsula of Mexico. They developed a complex civilization with magnificent temples, palaces, and observatories. Among their achievements were advances in mathematics and astronomy, as well as the creation of an accurate calendar.

The Maya used a system of numerals based on the number 20. Dots and dashes were used to write numbers, as shown below.

•	• •	• • •	• • • •	———	•———	• •———	• • •———	• • • •———	———
1	2	3	4	5	6	7	8	9	10

•	• •	• • •	• • • •	———	•———	• •———	• • •———	• • • •———
11	12	13	14	15	16	17	18	19

How did the Maya write numbers greater than 19? This was where the zero place holder was used. The Maya wrote their numbers in vertical columns with each row representing a power of 20. At most 19 units could go in any row. To write the number 20, the football-shaped zero symbol was placed in the bottom row and a single dot was placed above it. Here are some examples of Maya numbers.

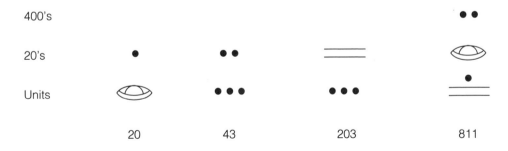

400's				• •
20's	•	• •	═══	⬭
Units	⬭	• • •	• • •	• ══
	20	43	203	811

The Maya used this system of numerals to record their astronomical observations. Ruins of Maya observatories show that the study of astronomy was well established. One group of temples at Uaxactun, Guatemala, had an obvious astronomical purpose. At sunrise on certain days of the year, the sun's rays passed through the temples and hit an observation point. Among other things, this allowed the Maya to determine the dates of the summer solstice and winter solstice (the days of the year with the longest and shortest durations of sunlight).

Multiculturalism in Mathematics, Science, and Technology

The Maya

The Early Days of Zero *(continued)*

With their knowledge of astronomy and their efficient number system, the Maya were able to devise an accurate calendar. The Maya concept of time was cyclical, with no beginning or end. Instead, there were three main time cycles that repeated regularly. Days on which these cycles coincided were of special importance to the Maya.

Questions for Critical Thinking

1. Why do you think the Maya chose the number 20 as the base for their number system?

   _____

   _____

   _____

2. How did the Maya's knowledge of astronomy help them develop an accurate calendar?

   _____

   _____

   _____

   _____

3. In addition to the dates of the summer solstice and winter solstice, what might the Maya have learned at the Uaxactun observatory?

   _____

   _____

   _____

   _____

4. The Maya concept of time consisted of several cycles that repeated over and over. Give an example of a cycle that is used in the modern calendar.

   _____

   _____

   _____

The Maya

Addition with Maya Numerals

Materials: pencil, beans (or unpopped popcorn), toothpicks (or coffee stirrers cut into fourths), pennies

Arithmetic with Maya numerals is similar to arithmetic with modern, Hindu-Arabic numerals. The following example shows how to add 241 and 166.

1. Begin by arranging beans and toothpicks (or similar objects) to form the numbers 241 and 166 with Maya numerals. Since there are twelve 20's in 241, with one unit left over, the beans and toothpicks should be arranged as shown below. Similarly, 166 contains eight 20's, with six units left over, leading to the arrangement shown.

```
400's


20's        • •              • • •
          _____        _____

Units         •                •
                            _____
            241      +      166      =
                                          ↑
                                         Sum
```

After each of Steps 1–4, record your results with Maya numerals in the "sum" column above.

2. To add the numbers, start at the bottom with the units row. Gather all of the beans and toothpicks in this row. There are two beans and one toothpick. This is a total of 7 units in the sum column.

3. Move up to the next row. Gather all of the beans and toothpicks in the 20's row. There are three toothpicks and five beans. This is a total of 20 units. Since each row can contain at most 19 units, put a zero marker (a penny) in the 20's row of the sum column and carry one bean to the 400's row.

4. Now gather all of the beans and toothpicks in the 400's row. There is just one bean, and this is placed in the sum column. The sum column contains one bean in the 400's row, a zero marker in the 20's row, and seven units. This number is 1(400) + 0(20) + 7 = 407.

5. Add 258 and 402 using Maya numerals. Use Maya numerals to record your work in the space provided.

```
400's


20's


Units
            258      +      402      =
```

The Maya

Maya Time Cycles

Materials: pencil, calculator

The modern calendar is based on the solar cycle—the amount of time it takes the earth to orbit the sun. It is a 365-day cycle. The Maya calendars were based on three different cycles, as summarized below.

- The religious calendar consisted of a 260-day cycle (13 months, each of 20 days).
- The solar calendar consisted of a 365-day cycle (18 months, each of 20 days, plus 5 extra days).
- The motion of the planet Venus provided an additional 584-day cycle.

Days on which cycles coincided were important to the Maya. Suppose a 365-day cycle and a 260-day cycle both begin today. How long will it be until these cycles again begin on the same day? Consider the following questions.

1. Suppose the cycles are 2 days long and 3 days long and both begin today. How many days will it take for them to be "in phase" (or coincide) again?

   _____

2. Suppose the cycles are 4 days long and 6 days long and both begin today. How many days will it take for them to be in phase again? (Be sure your answer is the *minimum* amount of time this will take.)

   _____

3. In general, given cycles of *n* days and *m* days, both beginning together, how can you find the minimum amount of time for the cycles to be in phase?

   _____

   _____

   _____

4. Suppose a 365-day cycle and a 260-day cycle both begin today. How many days will it be until the cycles are in phase again?

   _____

5. How many solar years is this? (This period of time was known to the Maya as the *calendar round*.)

   _____

Ynez Mexia

Tracking Biological Diversity

Mexican-American botanist and explorer **Ynez Mexia** (1870–1936) gathered over 100,000 specimens on her plant-collecting trips into remote regions of Mexico, Alaska, and South America. Traveling with only the help of local guides, she went into areas where plant collectors had never gone before and discovered many previously unknown plant species. The great variety of plants she found shows the biological diversity in the plant world. Her specimens brought thousands of new species to the attention of scientists, and have become an important part of the permanent collections of several universities and museums in the United States and Latin America.

Mexia's first major collecting trip was to the west coast of Mexico in September, 1926. She traveled by steamer to the port of Mazatlán and went south by train to the mountain valley town of Tepic. In Tepic, she hired horses and guides in order to explore the surrounding mountains. She later wrote that the vegetation in the area was so abundant and diverse that it was "hard to know where to begin to collect and even harder to know where to stop." After several weeks near Tepic, Mexia began to travel north on horseback with a pack train to carry her equipment and her specimens. As she gathered plant specimens, she also took many photographs. These photographs, showing plants in their natural environment, were invaluable to other scientists.

For seven months, Mexia continued to explore the rugged tropical mountains and valleys between Tuxpan and Puerto Vallarta. She often stayed at the homes of local people, recording the names and uses they had for local plants. In some cases, this led to the discovery of previously unknown species. For example, in the volcanic mountain area of Cruz de Vallarta, the local people told Mexia of a tall plant with small, pale-green leaves and tiny, greenish flowers. They called it *hierba de arlomo* and told her that it was a remedy for the poisonous bite of an insect called the *arlomo*. Mexia collected and cataloged this plant. It was later determined to be a previously unknown species and was named *Euphorbia mexiae* in her honor.

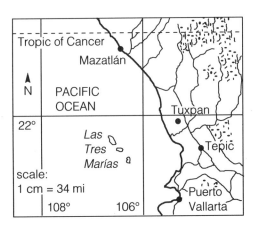

In 1928, Mexia collected 6,100 specimens during a short summer expedition to Alaska's Mt. McKinley. One year later, she traveled to Brazil to collect specimens in Minas Gerais for the State College of Agriculture there. After two years collecting in Minas Gerais, she organized a 4,800-km journey up the Amazon River. She traveled the first 4,000 km by steamer, disembarking in the Peruvian town of Iquitos. With hired horses and guides, Mexia set off to explore the area around the Rio Marañón, a large river that feeds into the Amazon. The rainy season left her stranded in the area for three months, but she used the time to explore the region by canoe, collecting specimens of plants, insects, and small birds. Altogether, Mexia collected over 65,000 plant specimens during two years in Peru and Brazil.

Ynez Mexia

Tracking Biological Diversity *(continued)*

Ynez Mexia was born in 1870 in Washington, D.C. Raised in Texas, she lived much of her adult life in Mexico. She operated a successful business in Mexico City for many years before she discovered her interest in science. When she began her study of botany, she was already fifty years old. While on an extended visit to San Francisco, she began taking nature trips with the Sierra Club. These nature trips prompted her to sign up for a college course in botany at the University of California, Berkeley. This and a few other courses were the only formal training in botany that Mexia received. She taught herself the techniques she needed for successful plant collecting and she sold her business in Mexico City to finance her expeditions. Her career lasted only from 1926 until her death in 1938, but in those twelve years Ynez Mexia made a lasting contribution to the understanding of biological diversity.

Questions for Critical Thinking

1. In your own words, explain what is meant by biological diversity.

    _____

    _____

    _____

2. Ynez Mexia took many photographs on her plant-collecting trips. What type of information might a scientist be able to gather from such photographs?

    _____

    _____

    _____

3. Why do you think Ynez Mexia brought back 65,000 plant specimens from the Amazon, but only 6,100 from Alaska?

    _____

    _____

4. Do you think it is important for scientists to record the common names that local people give to plants? Why or why not?

    _____

    _____

Ynez Mexia

A Plant Diversity Survey

Materials: pencil, eight large stakes (wood or metal), heavy string or twine, meter stick, field guide to local plants (optional)

Ynez Mexia traveled to many areas of the world to investigate plant diversity. In this activity, you will investigate plant diversity in an environment close to home. Choose an area that is not being cultivated and maintained by people, such an overgrown vacant lot, the bank of a stream, or another natural area.

Identifying Plant Diversity

1. When you locate an appropriate study area, have it approved by your teacher. When you have your teacher's approval, stake out an area of one square meter as shown in the illustration at the right. Wrap the string or twine around the stakes so that you have a "grid" of vegetation to study.

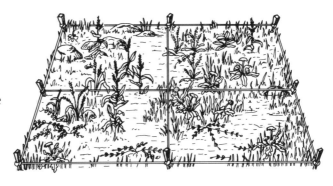

2. Describe the location and physical environment of your study area.

_____

_____

_____

3. Observe your grid closely. Make a list of all of the different plants you observe in the grid. At this point, do not try to identify these plants by their scientific names. Use common names if you know them or give your own descriptive names.

_____

_____

_____

_____

_____

_____

Ynez Mexia

A Plant Diversity Survey *(continued)*

Making a Plant-Distribution Map

4. Review your list of plants from Step 3. Assign a code number or initial to each type of plant that you found. Use your codes and the box below to make a map showing the location of each plant in your grid. You may want to color code your map.

5. How many different types of plants did you find in your survey?

_____

6. What factors may have influenced the variety of plants you found in your grid? Explain.

_____

_____

_____

7. What information can you infer from studying your plant-distribution map?

_____

_____

_____

Name _____ Date _____

The Native Americans I

Circles and Connections

T he idea that all the world is a circle was expressed by a Native-American elder of the Sioux Nation. He observed that tree trunks, bird nests, rain drops, and even the lodges (tepees) of the people were all organized on the principle of the circle. In the world view of Native-American peoples, nature is like a circle. The circle of nature is made up of many unique communities that interact as an integrated whole. This idea has many applications in understanding science.

From the smallest objects of study to the largest, circular patterns in nature occur over and over again. In the Bohr model of the atom, electrons follow a circular path around the atomic nucleus. In the solar system, planets follow elongated circular orbits around the sun. The diagrams at the right, illustrating the Bohr model of an atom and a simplified solar system, clearly show these circular patterns. Interacting forces keep electrons moving around the atomic nucleus and planets moving around the sun. When you observe galaxies or the rest of the stellar universe, you also observe circular patterns. These patterns conform to Native-American teachings that refer to the pattern of the universe as a circle.

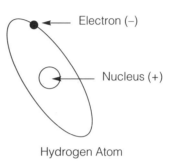

Hydrogen Atom

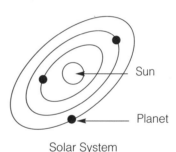

Solar System

Circular patterns are very important in the science of ecology. An *ecosystem* is an interacting network of living creatures and their surroundings. In such a network, oxygen, water, nutrients, and other elements are cycled and recycled many times. As these materials are cycled through living and non-living parts of the ecosystem, they follow the path of a circle.

A closer look at the oxygen-carbon dioxide cycle shows the parallel between ecological principles and the Native-American world view. A Native-American elder and teacher of the Chippewa nation has said that all creatures of the earth are related because all have the same mother (meaning the earth) and share the vital gifts that come from her. An example of this sharing can be found in the respiration patterns of plants and animals.

For example, imagine that you are standing in a grove of trees. You are inhaling oxygen and exhaling carbon dioxide. The plants, because of photosynthesis, are taking in the carbon dioxide and releasing oxygen. The requirements that all living creatures have for survival are shared in this way so that plants and animals share their life breath. This is consistent with both the Native-American view of relationships between living creatures and the ecological principles of cycling elements throughout the environment.

The Native Americans I

Circles and Connections *(continued)*

A contemporary scientist named James Lovelock made headlines in the scientific community by connecting the ecology of the earth with the ancient concept of *Gaia*. This view of the world suggests that the earth is one living organism or being. Native traditions throughout North America also express the belief that the earth is a living being. If you study the illustration at the right, you can see that there is a parallel between the way modern science interprets the structure of the earth and the way Native-American traditions view these same components. The breath of mother earth, her skin, bones, organs, and heart symbolize the atmosphere, crust, mantle, outer core, and molten core. Viewing the earth from this perspective promotes the idea that communities and individuals on Earth all have the same origin, or mother— that is, all living things are related.

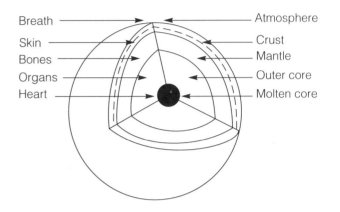

Questions for Critical Thinking

1. Give some other examples of circular patterns found in nature.

   _____

   _____

2. Describe an example of how you think human beings do not act as part of nature. Also describe an example of how you think human beings have a beneficial influence on nature.

   _____

   _____

3. If the earth functions like a single organism, all things have an important role to play in keeping the balance of nature. For example, rain waters plants, plants feed some animals, such as grasshoppers and mice, and these animals feed other animals, such as birds. What role do you think human beings have in nature?

   _____

   _____

The Native Americans I

Circles, Cycles, and Ecosystems

Materials: pencil

A forest and a pond represent two types of communities (or ecosystems) in nature. Study the illustration of a forest community shown below and answer the accompanying questions.

1. List six types of plants, animals, or other organisms that are found in the forest community.

   _____

   _____

   _____

2. Explain how the animals and plants of the forest community are connected to each other.

   _____

   _____

   _____

3. What needs of the forest plants and animals are supplied by the physical environment?

   _____

   _____

The Native Americans I

Circles, Cycles, and Ecosystems *(continued)*

The illustration below shows a pond community. Study the illustration and answer the accompanying questions.

4. List six types of plants or animals that are found in the pond community.

   _____

   _____

5. How are the animals and plants in the pond community connected to each other?

   _____

   _____

6. What needs of the pond plants and animals are supplied by the physical environment?

   _____

   _____

7. The oxygen-carbon dioxide cycle is an example in which the waste materials of one organism are essential for the survival of other organisms. Describe another example where this is true.

   _____

   _____

8. What would happen to a forest if nutrients were not recycled? What would happen to a pond?

   _____

   _____

The Native Americans II

Pan-American Agriculture

ver 40% of the food eaten by people throughout the world today comes from food plants developed by indigenous peoples of North and South America. Crops first developed by Native-American agriculturalists in the areas of present-day Mexico and Peru have become particularly important.

Over thousands of years of experience and experiments, Native Americans have developed, "invented," or domesticated more than forty crops important in agriculture today. These crops include corn, potatoes, tomatoes, squash, chocolate, avocados, peppers, sweet potatoes, artichokes, pumpkins, beans, vanilla, manioc (an edible root), pineapples, and blueberries. Some of these plants are illustrated at the right. This incredible agricultural diversity is evidence that indigenous peoples of the Americas conducted more plant experiments than any other people in the world.

During the fifteenth and sixteenth centuries, European explorers who visited the Americas brought samples of these "wonder" crops back to Europe and Asia. Since that time, Native-American agricultural crops have gained great worldwide popularity for their adaptability, nutrition, and flavor. Two crops in particular, corn and potatoes, have been especially successful and provide nourishment for millions of the world's people.

Corn (scientific names *Zea mays mexicana* and *Zea mays mays*) was developed by the early indigenous people of Mexico. It is considered a *cultigen* or an "invented" plant. The ancestral plant is thought to have been a wild grass from Central America known as *teosinte* (*teocintli*). Through thousands of years of experimentation and hybridization by Maya, Aztec, Inca, and North-American tribes, corn has evolved to grow only under human care—it cannot grow in the wild. Many hundreds of different strains of corn are known to have been developed under a wide variety of climatic conditions. Because of this history, corn can be grown in a large range of environments all over the world.

Potatoes (scientific name *Solanum tuberosum*) were first developed by indigenous people of the Andes mountains in present-day Peru. When the Europeans arrived, they discovered that the Andes tribes had developed over 300 different types of potatoes. Fewer than 250 types of potatoes still exist in the world today. However, research is taking place at several agricultural institutes in order to redevelop the native species from those that still exist. Today, commercial potato growers and agricultural researchers still visit the Andes to learn more about potatoes from the native people.

The Native Americans II

Questions for Critical Thinking

1. Make a list of everything that you have eaten during the past day. Be sure to list the basic ingredients that make up each food. For example, if you have eaten pizza, list it as cheese, tomato sauce, and wheat-flour crust.

_____

_____

_____

   Review your list and circle any foods that were originally developed by Native Americans. Calculate the percentage of your food items that were originally developed by Native Americans.

_____

2. What products, other than food, have come from crops originally developed by Native Americans?

_____

_____

_____

3. How have Native-American agricultural developments affected the rest of the world?

_____

_____

4. What evidence is there that experimentation was practiced by Native-American agriculturalists?

_____

_____

5. Why do you think many people are not aware of the agricultural contributions of Native Americans?

_____

_____

The Native Americans II

Growing Corn and Potatoes

Materials: pencil, 3 to 5 varieties of corn seed, 3 to 5 varieties of potatoes, dry soil (local or potting), 10 standard-size shoe boxes lined with plastic (waterproofed), spray bottle, graduated cylinder or other liquid metric measure, relief map of South America

How did Native-American agriculturalists develop strains of corn and potatoes that could flourish in so many environments? They began by developing new strains using cross-fertilization techniques. The new strains were then tested to see which types would grow best in different environments. In the following activity, you will test young corn and potato plants in ways that parallel the experiments of Native-American agriculturalists.

Preparing and Planting

1. Fill all of the shoe boxes with equal amounts of dry soil. Label five boxes for the corn seed experiments and five for the potatoes.

2. Prepare five identically-planted corn boxes for testing. Each corn box should have several rows of five seeds each. Each row should be a different seed variety. If you have three seed varieties, plant the rows lengthwise in the box as shown in the illustration at the right. If you have four or more varieties, plant the rows across the width of the box. Label the rows as shown.

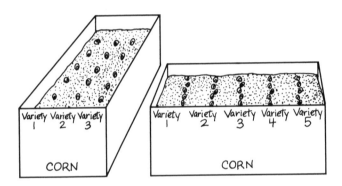

3. Assign each box a climate type. Label each box with its climate name and water allotment as shown below.

Climate Type	Water Allotment
Desert	10 mL
Temperate	30 mL
Swamp	60 mL
High Desert	126 mL
Jungle	250 mL

Multiculturalism in Mathematics, Science, and Technology

The Native Americans II

Growing Corn and Potatoes *(continued)*

4. Prepare the potatoes for planting by cutting them into small pieces. Make sure there is at least one "eye" in each piece. Plant and organize the five potato boxes as you did the corn boxes in Steps 2 and 3.

Testing the Seedlings

5. Using a spray bottle, water each box with the appropriate amount of water. Water each box every three days in a similar fashion.

6. Once a week, on the same day each week, dig up and observe a sample seed from each row. Carefully replace the seedling when you have completed your observations. Make a data chart like the one below to record your observations.

Plant: Corn
Week: 1

Variety	Length of Root	Length of Stem	General Appearance (Drawing)

7. After six to eight weeks, analyze your results. Report on which varieties of corn and potatoes did best and worst in each "environment." Summarize your results here.

_____

_____

_____

8. The Inca civilization included areas in present-day Ecuador, Peru, Bolivia, and Chile. Study these areas on a relief map of South America. If you were an agricultural experimenter in the Inca civilization and had just completed this experiment, where would you send each of your seed varieties to be grown? Why?

_____

_____

_____

_____

The Navajo I

Spider Woman Weaves a Rug

The Navajo are the largest tribe of Native Americans in the United States. Located mainly in Arizona, New Mexico, and Utah, the Navajo are famous throughout the world for their woven rugs and textiles.

The oldest Navajo textiles were blankets, done primarily in geometric patterns with the natural colors of sheep's wool: grey, cream, black, and brown. Some vegetable dyes also were used to produce shades of red. Back then, creating a blanket was a process of carding, spinning, dying, and weaving. In 1892, the Navajo began to sell the blankets commercially, but by the turn of the century, the Navajo blankets were being undersold by cheaper, mass-produced blankets. The market for Navajo blankets dwindled until weavers began making rugs. Today, Navajo weavers primarily make rugs. The use of synthetic dyes means more colors—such as purple and green—are available. Also, buying carded, dyed, and spun yarn saves time, so that weavers have more time to experiment with design and color.

In Navajo culture, the women are the weavers of rugs. Some men weave, but they are few. The women are credited with the artistic genius exhibited in the Navajo rug patterns. A mythical Navajo story says that Spider Man built the loom for Spider Woman. In the story, the sky, the earth, the sun, and lightning make up the parts of the loom.

In geometric rug patterns, shapes and lines are often repeated by sliding, flipping, shrinking, and enlarging. There are often many examples of line symmetry in the overall pattern as well as in smaller sections of the pattern. The borders generally feature a repeated pattern made by translations, or slides, along the edge.

The weaver usually does not draw a pattern on paper before weaving a rug. Instead, she mentally keeps track of the pattern at a very detailed level. To make this easier, the weaver positions the shapes of her design in a rectangular coordinate system. Written instructions for making the designs can be fairly complicated: "Weft on right, skip over 4, pick up first pair plus 2, skip 6, wrap around second pair, * skip 6, pick up 6, skip 6, wrap 2, repeat from * across warp, ending with pick up 4, skip 4."

Brenda Spencer is a Navajo weaver who comes from a family of well-known weavers. One of her rugs, in the traditional *burntwater* design, is illustrated at the right. Notice how the rug can be folded either horizontally or vertically to see its line symmetry. Also notice how smaller sections of the rug have their own symmetry. The border is formed by reflections and translations of a "stairway" design. With such complex designs, it is not surprising that Brenda Spencer often spends several months on one rug.

The Navajo I

Questions for Critical Thinking

1. Why do you think earth tones (grey, brown, cream, black, etc.) are so frequently used in Navajo blankets and rugs?

   _____

   _____

   _____

2. Navajo weavers seldom, if ever, repeat a rug pattern a second time. Why do you think this is the case?

   _____

   _____

   _____

3. What mathematical principles would be most useful to a Navajo rug weaver?

   _____

   _____

   _____

   _____

4. Why do you think weavers generally do not draw their patterns on paper before weaving?

   _____

   _____

   _____

5. Do you think the extensive use of symmetry found in so many Navajo rug designs makes it easier or more difficult to weave the rugs?

   _____

   _____

   _____

The Navajo I

Creating a Burntwater Design

Materials: colored pens, 18" by 24" sheet of paper or newsprint, ruler, cardboard, scissors

In the following activity you will make your own burntwater design. Begin with an 18" by 24" sheet of paper or newsprint.

1. Make a vertical fold to divide your paper in half. With the paper folded, make a horizontal fold to divide the paper in half again. Open the folded paper and lay it flat on the table. Use a blue pen or marker to draw your vertical and horizontal axes by tracing the fold lines.

2. On a piece of cardboard, draw a 3-step stairway, a 5-step stairway, an 8-step stairway, and a 13-step stairway as shown below. Each step of the stairways should be about one-half inch across and three-eighths of an inch deep. Cut out these pieces so that you can use them as templates.

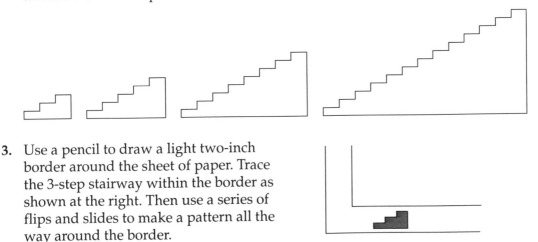

3. Use a pencil to draw a light two-inch border around the sheet of paper. Trace the 3-step stairway within the border as shown at the right. Then use a series of flips and slides to make a pattern all the way around the border.

4. Draw a steep diamond shape in the center of your pattern. (This shape is called the *hokha.*) Place the corner of the 13-step stairway at the intersection of the axes and trace the steps. Flip the 13-step stairway over one of the axes and trace the steps. Continue to flip and trace this template until you have completed the diamond shape.

5. You may wish to make smaller *hokha* in the center of your pattern by using the smaller templates and repeating the process in Step 4.

6. A stairway "mountain" shape can be made in each corner by using the 8-step stairway. Place the corner of the stairway in one of the right angles formed by the border guidelines. Trace around the entire edge of the template. Repeat this process by flipping the template over to the three other right angles.

7. You may wish to make smaller "mountain" designs by tracing smaller templates inside the outlines from Step 6.

8. Select four earth tones (brown, grey, dark red, etc.) and color in your rug design.

Multiculturalism in Mathematics, Science, and Technology   **129**

Name _____ Date _____

The Navajo I

Creating a Burntwater Design (continued)

Now that you have finished your rug design, answer the following questions.

1. Describe the different lines of symmetry in your design. Do any sections of the design have their own symmetry?

_____

_____

_____

_____

2. The stairways used to create your design had 3, 5, 8, and 13 steps. What is the next number in the sequence 3, 5, 8, 13...? Describe the rule for finding the next number in this sequence.

_____

_____

_____

_____

3. Describe at least three simple ways the design you created could be varied. That is, if you were starting over, how could you use the templates differently, but still produce a symmetric design?

_____

_____

_____

_____

_____

Name _____   Date _____

The Navajo II

Nature's First-Aid Kit

 Imagine yourself in the great outdoors, camping many miles away from the nearest doctor or hospital. What would you do if you accidentally cut yourself and had no access to commercial antiseptics for several days? The traditional plant medicine of the Navajo people may offer a solution.

One quarter of a million Navajo people (*Dine* in their own language, meaning "the people") comprise the Navajo Nation. The location of the Navajo Nation, which spans fourteen-million acres in the southwestern United States, is shown in the map at the right. For thousands of years, the knowledge of medicines found in plants has been passed on from generation to generation among the Navajo.

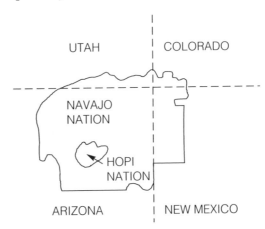

The Navajo, along with many other indigenous (native) peoples around the world, have developed great knowledge of medicines derived from plants. Many of these indigenous medical discoveries have been adopted and used in "western-style" or European medical practices. Over half of the medicines or pharmaceuticals used by medical doctors in the world today are based on plant medicines originally discovered by indigenous peoples. The most famous medicine discovered in this way may be *quinine*, for many centuries the only drug effective against malaria. The source of quinine is the bark of the cinchona tree, a plant used by indigenous peoples in Peru for thousands of years as a treatment for fevers.

Sam Martinez, a practicing Navajo medicine man, learned how to prevent infection in wounds from his grandparents. He knows that you can often find the necessary medicines in the wilderness. For example, to prevent infection in a cut, he would prescribe applications of pine pitch—the runny, sticky sap from pine trees. Martinez especially recommends pitch from pinyon pine trees (*Pinus edulis*, shown at the right) or ponderosa pine trees (*Pinus ponderosa*). These are the pine trees that grow in his local environment; however, Martinez says any species of pine will do, as long as it is a true pine and not a cedar.

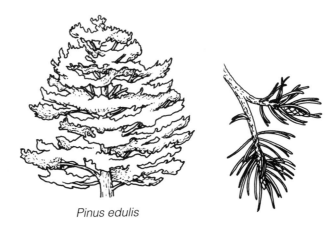

Pinus edulis

The Navajo II

Questions for Critical Thinking

1. What do you usually apply to cuts or wounds? Why?

   _____

   _____

2. How do you think pine pitch helps wounds heal?

   _____

   _____

3. Give some possible explanations of why pine needles produce a substance that heals wounds in humans. Why do you think pine trees have this, but cedar trees do not?

   _____

   _____

4. Of all the commonly used medicines, which ones may have been discovered by Native Americans or other indigenous people? Use your imagination or do some library research to find out more.

   _____

   _____

   _____

5. Researchers suggest that indigenous people in the world today may know of cures for various diseases. What diseases do you think might be curable with medicines discovered by indigenous people? Explain.

   _____

   _____

   _____

6. How would you suggest that the cures you discussed in Question 5 be researched and developed? To whom should the credit go?

   _____

   _____

Name _____   Date _____

Pine Pitch Antiseptic

Materials: pencil, small container of pine pitch, 12 drops of bacterial culture (*Staphylococcus aureus*, provided by your teacher), two petri dishes filled with nutrient agar, one wire loop, forceps or tweezers, masking tape, laboratory burner (or lighter or matches), 8 sterile filter-paper disks, petroleum jelly (optional)

Navajo medicine man Sam Martinez cures his patients' wounds with pine pitch antiseptic. As you may know, you should never try any medicine without the direct guidance of an appropriate medical professional. Yet, without applying it to yourself, how can you prove the effectiveness of this medicine? Though the following laboratory activity, you will discover, and experimentally verify, the effectiveness of this Navajo antiseptic. To do this, you will test whether pine pitch can inhibit the growth of infection-causing bacteria.

Testing Your Antiseptic

Safety Note: You will be working with open flames and a concentrated suspension of bacteria commonly found on the skin and in the environment. To be safe and to get good results follow, these precautions.

- **Wash** your hands thoroughly before and after this activity.
- Do **not** touch your mouth or any sores during this activity.
- Open the petri dishes **only** when instructed and for the shortest possible time.
- Tie back loose hair and clothing. Use care in handling flames and hot objects.

1. Obtain two petri dishes filled with nutrient agar. Use small pieces of masking tape to label both dishes with your name and class period. Then label one dish "PINE PITCH" and the other "NO PINE PITCH."

2. Your teacher will briefly open the tops of your petri dishes and place six drops of the bacterial solution into the center of each dish. The name of this bacteria is *Staphylococcus aureus*. It is a common cause of bacterial infection in cuts and wounds.

3. Hold the wire loop in a flame from a laboratory burner, match, or lighter for approximately ten seconds. This technique, shown at the right, is called "flaming." Flaming sterilizes the metal so there are no unwanted bacteria on the loop.

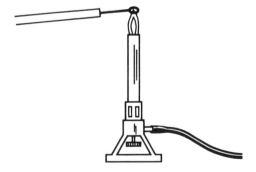

4. Using your sterile wire loop, BRIEFLY open each petri dish one at a time and gently but thoroughly spread the bacteria over the nutrient agar. Be careful not to tear the surface of the agar. When you have finished, flame your loop again so that you do not transfer the bacteria to other surfaces.

Multiculturalism in Mathematics, Science, and Technology

The Navajo II

Pine Pitch Antiseptic *(continued)*

5. Sterilize the tips of your forceps by flaming them. Open the dish marked "NO PINE PITCH." Using the sterile forceps, place four of the sterile filter-paper disks on the agar in the petri dish. Cover the dish immediately. This dish will be your experimental control.

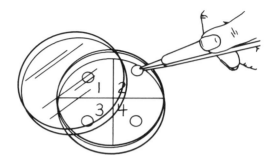

6. Sterilize the tips of your forceps again. This time, flame them for fifteen seconds. Using the hot, sterile forceps, dip a sterile filter-paper disk into the pine pitch. The pine pitch will form a sticky glob on the disk. Place the pitch-covered paper disk in one quadrant of the petri dish labeled "PINE PITCH." The forceps need to be hot enough so that the pitch will not act like glue. Repeat this procedure until there are four disks in the dish, similar to the illustration for Step 5. Cover the dish immediately when finished. (Tip: If the pitch is so sticky that you cannot release the disk, try dipping the forceps in petroleum jelly before picking up another disk.)

7. Tape down the covers of your petri dishes and give the dishes to your teacher. Your dishes will be kept in a warm place for incubation for 24 to 48 hours. What do you predict will happen in each of your dishes?

_____

8. After 24 to 48 hours, carefully inspect your petri dishes. Do not open them. In the space below, make detailed drawings of what you see in each dish. When you have finished, return the unopened dishes to your teacher who will dispose of them.

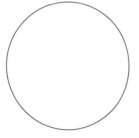 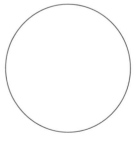

9. Describe any differences you observe between the dishes.

_____

_____

10. Does the pine pitch have any effect on the growth of bacteria? How can you tell?

_____

_____

Hideyo Noguchi

Disease Detective

r. Hideyo Noguchi (1876–1928) is well known for his research on a variety of diseases, their causes, and their cures. He directed his energies to the study of yellow fever, syphilis, Rocky Mountain spotted fever, infectious jaundice, trachoma, and oroya fever. Other diseases in which he was interested included polio, influenza, rabies, and herpes.

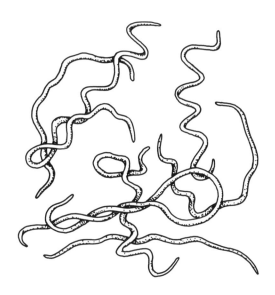

Dr. Noguchi's most important achievement involved the study of syphilis, a sexually transmitted disease. He was the first person to obtain pure laboratory cultures of the organism that causes syphilis, *Treponema pallidum*, shown in the illustration at the right. Dr. Noguchi also showed that *T. pallidum* was the cause of a previously unexplained form of paralysis. He did this by finding the organism in the cerebrospinal fluid of paralyzed patients. Dr. Noguchi made many improvements in the laboratory test for detecting syphilis. Improving the test was important for early detection of the disease. With early detection, infected people could be treated before their bodies were seriously damaged and before they spread the disease to others.

In addition to his work on syphilis, Dr. Noguchi authored an important book on the venoms of poisonous snakes. He also devised methods for growing pure cultures of various types of bacteria.

Seisaku Hideyo Noguchi was born in Inawashiro, Fukushima, Japan on November 24, 1876. Inawashiro was a small farming village and Noguchi's parents were very poor. A childhood accident involving an *urori* (a charcoal burner used to heat water) seriously damaged his left hand, leaving it malformed and practically useless. Despite his circumstances, Noguchi excelled in all his studies at the local lower and middle schools. After graduation, he found an apprenticeship as a pharmacist and paramedic at a small nearby medical clinic.

Noguchi found himself attracted to medicine and read all the books and journals at the clinic. He worked at the clinic and studied medical books unti! his employer thought he was ready to take the initial medical license examination. Noguchi left for Tokyo at the age of 20, passed the initial examination, and enrolled at a private medical school. After one year at the medical school he was able to pass the final examination and became a licensed doctor. The young Dr. Noguchi had varied interests and wished to pursue his education further by studying abroad. He began his research career at the Kitasato Institute of Infectious Diseases in Tokyo.

Hideyo Noguchi

Disease Detective *(continued)*

At the Kitasato Institute, Noguchi met a visitor from the United States, Dr. Simon Flexner. Dr. Flexner casually mentioned to Noguchi that he should come to the United States to do research. A few months later, Dr. Noguchi boarded a steamer and arrived at Dr. Flexner's residence in Philadelphia. Soon after, the Carnegie Foundation gave Dr. Noguchi a grant to study in Copenhagen at the Staatens Serum Institut. When he returned to the United States, Dr. Flexner, now his mentor, invited him to work at the new Rockefeller Institute for Medical Research in New York City. It was at the Rockefeller Institute where Dr. Noguchi did his most important work on *T. pallidum.*

In addition to his other work, Dr. Noguchi spent many years trying to determine the cause of yellow fever. In 1918, he thought that he had discovered the organism, but his results turned out to be false. His research on yellow fever took him all over the world and finally led him to Accra, Ghana (then called the Gold Coast). However, before he had a chance to do research, he caught the disease and died there on May 21, 1928. It was not until 1938 that the cause of yellow fever was discovered to be a virus.

Questions for Critical Thinking

1. Historically, microbiologists have classified bacteria into groups based on their overall cell shape. Examples of the three main groups are shown at the right. Dr. Noguchi studied the organism *Treponema pallidum.* To which of these groups does *T. pallidum* belong? Explain.

Cocci   Spirilla   Baccilli (rods)

_____

_____

_____

2. Cerebrospinal fluid is a clear, colorless, watery fluid that surrounds the brain and spinal cord. It acts as a "shock absorber," protecting the delicate brain and spinal cord from injury. Dr. Noguchi determined that some patients suffering from a mysterious form of paralysis had *T. pallidum* growing in their cerebrospinal fluid. Why might this have caused these people to become paralyzed?

_____

_____

_____

_____

Hideyo Noguchi

Bacterial Growth

Materials: pencil, calculator (optional)

A single bacterium reproduces by dividing into two bacteria. This process, shown in the illustration at the right, is known as *fission*. All of the essential cell machinery is duplicated beforehand so that each new cell is an exact copy of the parent. As this process occurs over and over again, the bacteria are said to be "growing." What this really means is that they are increasing in number.

Dr. Hideyo Noguchi's research concentrated on disease-causing bacteria. People infected with disease-causing bacteria get sicker as the bacteria multiply. To cure these diseases, bacterial growth must be stopped. Antibiotic drugs that are used to treat diseases stop bacterial growth by interfering with some step in the process of fission. Penicillin, an antibiotic used in the treatment of syphilis and other bacterial infections, interferes with the process of building new cell walls.

In this activity, you will set up a bacterial "growth chart" to examine how fast the number of bacteria increases when they are allowed to grow unchecked.

Growth Data

1. Suppose a type of bacteria divides every twenty minutes. Fill in the chart below.

Time in Minutes	Number of Divisions	Number of Bacteria
0	0	1
20	1	2
	2	
	3	
	4	
	5	
	6	
	7	
	8	

Multiculturalism in Mathematics, Science, and Technology

Hideyo Noguchi

Bacterial Growth *(continued)*

Graphing Bacterial Growth

2. Construct a graph of the growth data using the axes provided below.

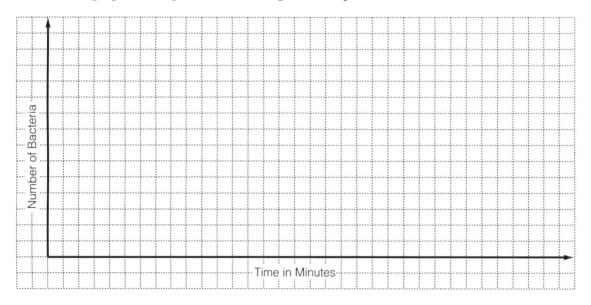

3. Based on your data, how many bacteria do you predict there will be after 6 hours. Show your calculations below.

_____

_____

4. Based on your graph, what do you think will happen to the number of bacteria as time goes on?

_____

_____

5. Can the number of bacteria continue to increase indefinitely? Why or why not?

_____

_____

Extension

6. Develop a general formula for calculating the number of bacteria after *n* divisions.

_____

Srinivasa Ramanujan

An Infatuation with Infinity

ave you ever wondered about infinity? In mathematics, the infinite is commonplace. Many decimal numbers, sequences, and figures go on and on without end. The brilliant mathematician **Srinivasa Ramanujan** (Shree nee VA sa Ra MA noo jun) understood infinity as few people ever have or ever will.

Srinivasa Ramanujan was born in southern India in 1887 and lived much of his life in poverty and obscurity. He was largely self-taught, with mathematics his only real interest. He recorded his mathematical discoveries in a notebook that he carried with him and showed to anyone who expressed an interest. Ramanujan neglected other subjects and never graduated from college due to his lack of proficiency in English, a required subject.

Ramanujan married in 1909 and barely managed to support himself and his wife. He held several menial jobs for which he earned a pittance. In 1913, at the urging of his friends, Ramanujan wrote to three of England's foremost mathematicians. In these letters, Ramanujan described over one hundred theorems from various branches of mathematics. Most of the theorems were derived by intuition, without any coherent proof.

Although two of Ramanujan's letters were returned unopened, the third was read by G. H. Hardy of Cambridge University. Hardy was one of the finest mathematicians in the world, yet he was astonished by the insight of Ramanujan's work. Hardy recognized that this was the work of an amazing mathematical talent and once said of Ramanujan's theorems that they "must be true, because if they were not true, no one would have had the imagination to invent them." Thus began an extraordinary, five-year collaboration of two men who had little in common except a love of mathematics.

During his five-year collaboration with Hardy, Ramanujan published more than thirty papers on such topics as pi, infinite series, prime and composite numbers, integers as the sum of squares, function theory, and combinatorics. Ramanujan wrote with amazing originality and depth on a wide range of topics in mathematics. His theorems eventually influenced cancer research, pyrometry (the study of very high temperatures), and statistical mechanics.

Ramanujan fell ill in 1917 and died in 1919 at age 32. More than 70 years after his death, his work is still an important source of new mathematical ideas. For example, in the 1970's one of Ramanujan's identities was used by computer programmers to calculate millions of digits in the decimal expansion of pi. The identity provided a more efficient method for this calculation than had previously been known. Today, there are still areas of Ramanujan's work that have not been fully explored. However, his notebooks are just now being published to the delight of modern-day mathematicians.

Srinivasa Ramanujan

Questions for Critical Thinking

1. What were some hardships that Ramanujan had to overcome to be recognized as a brilliant mathematician?

   _____

   _____

   _____

2. What made the partnership of Ramanujan and Hardy so improbable?

   _____

   _____

   _____

3. Ramanujan is acknowledged as a genius in the field of mathematics, yet he could not graduate from college. Do you feel that Ramanujan should have been awarded a diploma? Why or why not?

   _____

   _____

   _____

4. Ramanujan is credited with discovering several formulas that give very efficient and accurate approximations for pi (π). Why is it useful to have formulas for approximating pi?

   _____

   _____

   _____

5. Ramanujan was largely self-taught. What are some advantages and disadvantages to learning a subject this way?

   _____

   _____

   _____

Srinivasa Ramanujan

Circles and Pi

Materials: pencil, assorted circular objects, each at least three inches in diameter (soup cans, pots, glasses, etc.), tape measure, calculator

Srinivasa Ramanujan produced hundreds of mathematical theorems on topics as varied as infinite series, prime numbers, and combinatorics. He was also very interested in the concept of π (pi). The following activity will give you experience in working with circles and π.

1. Collect a variety of circular objects such as those listed above. For each object, use a tape measure to measure the circumference and the diameter. Record the measurements in the appropriate columns of the table the below.

Object	Circumference (C)	Diameter (D)	$C \div D$

2. Use a calculator to help fill in the remaining column of the table.

3. Do you see a pattern? If so, describe it.

_____

_____

_____

4. Pi is defined as the ratio of a circle's circumference to its diameter. Do you think this is the same number for all circles? If so, give an estimate for the number π based on your above results.

_____

_____

_____

Srinivasa Ramanujan

A Geometric Method of Estimating Pi

Materials: pencil, compass, calculator

One of the topics that interested Srinivasa Ramanujan was π (pi), the ratio of any circle's circumference to its diameter. The following activity is a simple, geometric method of estimating the value of π. It uses the 50 by 50 array of dots below.

1. Place your compass point on the dot labeled A below. Open the compass to the dot labeled B and draw an arc to the dot labeled C.

2. Suppose the distance from dot A to dot B is r. What is the area of the quarter circle you drew in Step 1 in terms of r?

_____

3. What is the area of the square array in terms of r?

_____

4. Find the ratio of the area of the quarter circle to the area of the square array.

_____

5. How many dots are there in the quarter circle? How many are in the square array?

_____

6. Divide the number of dots in the quarter circle by the number of dots in the square array.

_____

7. What must be done with your result in Step 6 to find an estimate for pi? What value does this give?

_____

_____

Eloy Rodriguez

Chemicals from Nature

I s there "chemistry" between Latin-American herbology, pharmaceutical companies, and chimpanzees? **Dr. Eloy Rodriguez,** a Mexican-American professor of biology and chemistry, investigates such questions in his laboratory and in the field. Since the 1970's, Dr. Rodriguez and his colleague, Dr. Manuel Aregullin, have researched and isolated chemicals from plants. Often, they first learn of the beneficial properties of plants from various experts ranging from their grandparents to resourceful chimpanzees.

Through his family and community, Dr. Rodriguez recognized the long-established knowledge of herbology in his Latin American heritage. Knowledge of the medicinal qualities of plants in the southwestern United States, the Caribbean, Central America, and South America, was first developed by the indigenous people of these areas and then adopted by the Spanish. The use of herbs to cure a variety of illnesses indicates the presence of medically effective chemicals in the plants. Some of these herbs, such as mint, oregano, cinnamon bark, and chamomile, may be familiar to you. Dr. Rodriguez and Dr. Aregullin are experts at isolating the effective chemicals in such herbs.

Although clues usually come from the medicinal-plant knowledge of indigenous people, medicinal plants can also be found by observing the behavior of animals. A recent clue came from the eating habits of wild chimpanzees in Tanzania. An anthropologist observed that chimpanzees showing signs of illness collected and ate special leaves. He sent a sample of these leaves to Dr. Rodriguez. From these leaves, Dr. Rodriguez and his colleagues isolated a rare chemical called thiarubrine-A, and learned that it has strong antibiotic properties. The illustration at the right shows Dr. Rodriguez holding a molecular model of thiarubrine-A. It is interesting to note that this same chemical has been found in a medicinal plant used by native people in Canada.

Once a chemical such as thiarubrine-A has been isolated from a plant, it can serve as a "lead" or model chemical for a pharmaceutical company to synthesize or create artificially. These synthetic chemicals are tested and often developed into medical drugs. Synthetic drugs or medicines from pharmacies are much stronger than chemicals originally found in nature. Dr. Aregullin has observed that nature rarely produces strong, toxic chemicals; herbal remedies tend to be more gentle and nontoxic. However, Dr. Rodriguez cautions that any remedy should be from a reliable source and if people who know little about herbal medicines "just go out and pluck, they're going to get themselves into problems."

Eloy Rodriguez

Questions for Critical Thinking

1. Think about the times when you have had indigestion, a cold, the flu, a sore throat, or some other minor ailment. Are there any herbal or "family" remedies you commonly use at such times? List them below and explain their use.

   _____

   _____

2. How do you think indigenous people of North and South America first discovered the medicinal qualities of plants?

   _____

   _____

   _____

3. Some people think herbal remedies are better for your body than commercial pharmaceuticals. What are some arguments for and against this point of view?

   _____

   _____

   _____

4. Why do you think Dr. Rodriguez and Dr. Aregullin chose to spend their careers researching the medicinal herbs used by Hispanics and other cultures?

   _____

   _____

   _____

5. Dr. Rodriguez warns that people who "just go out and pluck" herbs are going to have problems. What are some problems that could occur if people gather herbs for medicine without expert advice?

   _____

   _____

   _____

Eloy Rodriguez

Analyzing Herbs

Materials: pencil, Hispanic herbal remedies, such as yerba buena, mint, oregano, cinnamon bark, chamomile, etc., isopropyl alcohol, acetone, water, beakers or wide-mouth jars, Whatman chromatography paper or heavy coffee-filter paper, paper clips, thin rod (glass rod, wooden dowel, or pencil), parafilm or plastic wrap, capillary tube (thin pipette or modified medicine dropper), mortar and pestle (optional), hot plate (optional)

In the following activity, you will perform a technique that Dr. Rodriguez uses in his laboratory. This chromatographic technique is used as a method of isolating chemical compounds from plants such as yerba buena, mint, oregano, cinnamon bark, and chamomile. You may choose to bring in one of these herbs from home for your experiment.

Depending on the type of herb you have chosen, you will decide on the type of herbal extraction and solvent mixture to use in the following procedure. Suggestions for extraction and solvent mixtures are given below. Study these methods before you proceed.

Making an Extract

The most common extraction method in herbal medicine is to boil the herb in hot water. The finished extract is usually called a *tea*. You can make the extract very concentrated by using large amounts of the herb and/or boiling the mixture for a long time. Another type of extract is made by using a mortar and pestle to grind the herb with a solvent such as alcohol or acetone. **Safety Note:** Solvents such as acetone and alcohol are highly flammable. Use these only in well-ventilated areas and away from open flames. Boiling liquids can cause serious burns. Handle them carefully to avoid splashes.

Separating the Extract on a Chromatogram

1. Cut several pieces of chromatography paper into 2-cm by 5-cm strips. When handling chromotography paper, hold it by its edges to avoid getting your finger oils into your chromatogram. Draw a thin pencil line 1 cm above the bottom edge of the paper. Fill the bottom of a beaker with solvent (acetone or isopropyl alcohol) to a depth of 1 cm. Cover the jar with parafilm or plastic wrap so that it is airtight.

2. Fill a thin capillary tube with your herbal extract. The tube will fill itself by capillary action if you immerse one end. Using the capillary tube, place one very small dot of your herbal extract just above the pencil line you drew in Step 1.

3. Place a bent paper clip through the top edge of the strip as shown at the right. Open the wrapping on the beaker and place a rod across it. Hang the paper clip with the strip attached as shown. Carefully cover the opening again so it is airtight. Be sure not to move the beaker or slosh the contents.

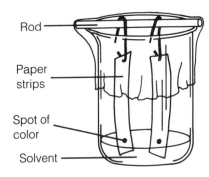

Eloy Rodriguez

Analyzing Herbs *(continued)*

4. Let the wrapped beaker sit undisturbed. You will begin to see the solvent travel up the paper strip. As it moves, it will "drop off" different substances from the extract along the way. You may begin to see some of these substances as different-colored bands on the paper strip. Chemists can identify these substances by measuring exactly how far they move along the chromatogram.

Your challenge in this activity is to experiment with different extraction methods and solvents to achieve the best chromatographic separation for your herb. To decide which techniques to use, it may help you to study the characteristics of your herb.

5. Carefully observe the characteristics of the herb you have chosen. Name the herb and record your observations about it in the space below.

_____

_____

_____

6. Draw your herb in the space at the right. List any parts of the plant that you can identify.

After experimenting with different extraction techniques and solvents for separation, answer the following questions.

7. Draw the results of your best separation in the space at the right.

8. What did you do to achieve the best separation?

_____

_____

9. From your chromatographic analysis, what can you conclude about your herb?

_____

_____

The Sami

A Snow-Travel Solution

Far north of the Arctic Circle, in the "land of the midnight sun," live the **Sami** people. Previously known as Lapps or Laplanders, *Sami*—from their own language—is their preferred name. The land of the Sami stretches across northern Norway, Sweden, Finland, and the northwest corner of the Soviet Union. The men and women of the Sami culture are related to ethnic Norwegians, Swedes, Finns, and Russians. However, the Sami have kept their traditional lifestyles. Specialized Sami cultures have developed in each of the three main environments found in their land: mountains, coastline, and forest. Although these cultures vary somewhat, all three depend on the reindeer for milk, meat, and other materials. Also, all three must contend with snow.

The Arctic north is covered with snow for more than half the year. This situation poses many challenges, especially to mobility. The indigenous Sami solved the problem of snow travel more than 3000 years ago when they invented the *savih*, known today as a ski. Well-preserved skis, more than 3500 years old, have been found in Finland and Norway. These skis distinctly resemble Sami skis used today. The illustration at the right shows a 4000-year-old rock carving from Norway. It is the oldest known representation of a person skiing.

Sami men and women use skis through all types of snow for travel, hunting, herding reindeer, and other transportation needs. On skis, hunters can overtake a bear, wolverine, or wild reindeer. For 3000 years, Sami herdsmen have traveled on skis when tending their reindeer. Some herdsmen carry one long pole that they use for maneuvering, as well as for herding and hunting reindeer. This is illustrated at the right in a drawing from around 1660. Other herdsmen use two poles to increase their speed. Several Sami groups use no poles, as they are pulled along on skis by one of their reindeer. Racing on skis drawn by reindeer is a favorite Sami sport.

Originally, skis were not practical for reindeer racing because their structure resembled that of snowshoes. These first skis were short and broad. As the Sami improved the design, the skis became longer and the tips were pointed and turned upward. Usually, heat was used to curve and press the wood— a process known in the Sami language as *tsik tih*. Often, fir or birch wood was used. In addition, some types of skis had leather covers, while others were waxed underneath with pine pitch or grease.

There are many distinct styles of skis in the the land of the Sami, as well as in the rest of the world. The invention of skis by these indigenous people of Scandinavia has led to many practical applications and a popular sport. Today, some of the top professional skiers in the sports world design and make their own skis.

The Sami

Questions for Critical Thinking

1. Why was the development of skis important to the Sami? Why was it important to the rest of the world?

    _____

    _____

    _____

2. What other adaptations or inventions might Sami men and women have made for living in snow?

    _____

    _____

    _____

3. Why is the shape and length of a ski important? What shape do you think is fastest? What shape do you think is slowest? Explain your answers.

    _____

    _____

    _____

4. Study the illustrations on the previous page. How have skis changed in 3000 years?

    _____

    _____

    _____

5. Why did the Sami put grease or pine pitch on the bottom of their skis? Why did they curve the wood so that the toes turned upward?

    _____

    _____

    _____

The Sami

Ski-Design Testing

Materials: balsa wood (thin piece, approximately 7.5 cm by 20 cm), razor knife with handle, string (7- or 8-cm piece), masking tape, standard mass (200 g), three 10-pound bags of flour, four cardboard box "bottoms" (the type that holds four beverage six-packs and measures 25.5 cm by 35.5 cm by 6.5 cm), spring balance (marked in newtons), steam-heat source, hot pad or towel, melted wax

The Sami ski-makers developed and tested their ski designs in natural snow fields. In this activity, you will build a model snowfield and use it to develop new ski designs. As you modify your model skis, you will test the modifications using basic scientific tools, techniques, and measurements.

Making a Model Snowfield

Open out one end flap on two of the box bottoms. On the other two, open out both end flaps. Fit all four box bottoms together to make one long box and tape them together. Fill the long box with flour to make your "snowfield" as illustrated below.

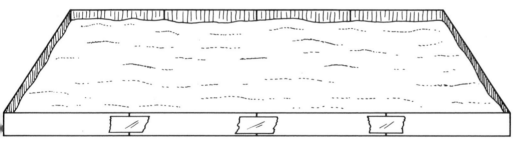

Making and Testing a Model Ski

1. Using the razor knife, cut the balsa wood to the dimensions given in the materials list. This piece of wood will serve as a crude ski. (**Safety Note:** A razor knife can cause serious wounds. Handle the knife carefully and always cut in the direction away from any part of your body.)

2. Securely tape the string to one end of the ski, and tie the loose end of the string to the hook or loop on the spring scale.

3. Place the wooden ski onto one end of the model snowfield. Place the 200-gram standard mass on the *center* of the the ski. If necessary, use tape to secure the mass. This mass represents the weight of a human on the ski.

4. As one person observes the scale measurements, another person should use the scale to pull the ski along the model snowfield at a constant speed. As the ski approaches the end of the snowfield, note and record the scale measurement in newtons. Record the measurement below.

_____

The Sami

Ski-Design Testing (continued)

5. Did your model stay on top of the snow? Describe what happened.

_____

_____

6. Did this affect the measurement in any way? Explain.

_____

7. Calculate the friction coefficient, μ (the Greek letter *mu*), by dividing the force (F) by the load (L). The force is your scale reading and the load is 200 grams. Show your work below. (Hint: The value of μ that you calculate should be less than 1.)

_____

Testing New Ski Designs

8. The earliest skis were short and broad like the model you made in Step 1. Now make your model ski long and thin by cutting it down to a width of 2 cm. Trim one end to a V shape. Fasten the 200-gram weight to the new ski and repeat Step 4. Record your measurements and observations. Calculate the friction coefficient, μ, for this ski.

_____

9. Hold the pointed end of your ski (about one third of the total length) over steam. (**Safety Note:** Hot steam can cause serious burns. Keep your hands and face away from the steam.) After steaming the end of the ski for a few minutes, pull it out of the steam and gently bend the tip upward using a hot pad or folded towel. You may have to steam and bend the ski several times to get it to resemble the curve shown in previous illustrations. Repeat Step 4 and record your measurements and observations. Calculate the friction coefficient, μ, for the bent-tip ski.

_____

10. Coat the bottom of your ski with melted wax provided by your teacher. Allow the wax to harden. Repeat Step 4 and record your measurements and observations. Calculate the friction coefficient, μ, for the waxed ski.

_____

11. Summarize your findings in a laboratory report. Remember that the higher the value of the friction coefficient, μ, the greater the friction. In your conclusions, discuss how the Sami improved on their invention. Support your discussion with numerical data and observations from your experiment.

Seki Kowa

Solving the Unsolvable

eki Kowa was born in 1642 in Edo (now Tokyo), Japan. His father, Nagaakira Utiyama, was a samurai (a member of Japan's military class). However, the child was adopted by a patriarch of the Seki family who was an accountant, and, at an early age, Seki Kowa showed great mathematical aptitude. He was largely self-taught and he was a remarkable problem-solver. From these beginnings, Seki went on to become the greatest Japanese mathematician of the 17th century.

An earlier mathematician, Kazuyuki Sawaguchi, was reportedly the first Japanese mathematician to master Chu Shih-Chieh's *t'ien-yuan shu* ("method of the celestial element") for solving systems of equations. In 1670, Kazuyuki wrote seven volumes on this topic and concluded the seventh volume with fifteen problems that he believed were unsolvable by means of *t'ien-yuan shu*. In 1674, Seki Kowa published solutions to all fifteen of Kazuyuki's "unsolvable" problems. Seki's solutions were so profound that no mathematician was able to understand what he had done. Katahiro Takebe, a distinguished student of Seki, eventually wrote a book in 1685 to explain Seki's method.

Among his many achievements, Seki Kowa improved upon the Chinese methods of solving higher-degree equations. He also developed the use of determinants in solving simultaneous equations and is credited with inventing a calculus native to 17th-century Japan. This early form of the calculus is known as the *yenri* ("circle principal"). *Yenri* was a method of finding the area of a circle by dividing the circle into many small approximating rectangles. The figure shown at the right, created by one of Seki Kowa's students, illustrates the *yenri* method.

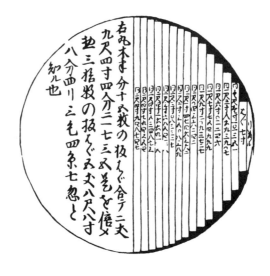

Seki Kowa's students were especially important in spreading his achievements. Some of Seki's principal theorems were kept secret and shared only with his most trusted students. After his death, Seki Kowa's pupils collected and published these theorems in a work entitled *Katuyo Sanpo.*

Throughout his life, Seki had a reputation as a brilliant mathematician and an inspirational teacher. He had a tremendous influence on his students and is credited with awakening the scientific spirit in Japan that continues to thrive today. In 1907, almost two hundred years after Seki's death, the Emperor of Japan honored Seki for his efforts to give the people of Japan a knowledge of the mathematical sciences. It was the highest posthumous award ever given to a mathematician.

Seki Kowa

Questions for Critical Thinking

1. Do you think Seki Kowa's life might have been different if he had been raised as the son of a samurai rather than as the son of an accountant?

   _____

   _____

   _____

2. Why do you think Seki Kowa kept many of his theorems secret from all but his most trusted students?

   _____

   _____

   _____

3. One of the "unsolvable" problems posed by Kazuyuki Sawaguchi was the following.

   Three circles are inscribed in a circle, each tangent to the other two and to the original circle. They cover all but 120 square units of the circumscribing circle. The diameters of the two smaller inscribed circles are equal, and each is five units less than the than the diameter of the larger inscribed circle. Find the diameters of the three inscribed circles.

   Explain how Seki Kowa might have gone about solving this problem. (You do not need to solve it!)

   _____

   _____

   _____

   _____

4. In the *yenri* method, why do you think rectangles are used to help find the area of a circle?

   _____

   _____

   _____

   _____

Seki Kowa

Determinants and Systems of Equations

Materials: pencil

There are many ways to solve a system of two equations in two unknowns. You may already be familiar with the substitution method, the addition method, and the graphing method. Another efficient method of solving systems of equations uses **determinants.** This is the method of Seki Kowa.

To use determinants, the system must be in the standard form shown below.

$$a_1x + b_1y = c_1$$
$$a_2x + b_2y = c_2$$

The determinant, D, is calculated from the coefficients as follows.

$$D = a_1b_2 - a_2b_1$$

1. Find the determinant of each of the systems of equations below.

    $3x + 6y = 3$ $4x - 3y = 22$
    $5x + 7y = -1$ $-x - 2y = -11$

    $D =$ _____ $D =$ _____

2. Once the determinant has been calculated, the solution to the system of equations can be found with the following formulas.

    $$x = \frac{c_1b_2 - b_1c_2}{D} \qquad\qquad y = \frac{a_1c_2 - c_1a_2}{D}$$

    Use the method of determinants to solve each of the following systems of equations.

    $3x + 6y = 3$ $4x - 3y = 22$
    $5x + 7y = -1$ $-x - 2y = -11$

    Solution: _____   Solution: _____

3. Does the method of determinants work for any system of equations? Does it work if the determinant is 0? Explain.

    _____

    _____

    _____

    _____

    _____

Seki Kowa

The *Yenri* Method

Materials: pencil, compass, extra sheets of paper, ruler, index card, calculator

Seki Kowa is credited with developing the *yenri* method to find the area of a circle. The following activity will give you an idea of how the method works.

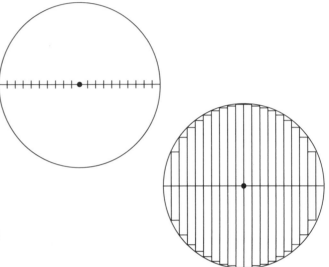

1. Open your compass to 10 cm and draw a circle on a separate sheet of paper.

2. Draw a horizontal diameter in your circle. Mark off one-centimeter lengths from the center of the circle as shown at the right.

3. Draw vertical chords through each of the points marked off in Step 2. You may wish to use the corner of an index card to be sure that the vertical lines are perpendicular to the diameter.

4. Draw horizontal segments to form rectangles as shown at the right. You should have 18 rectangles.

5. Each rectangle has a width of 1 cm. Measure the height of each rectangle and record your results on a separate sheet of paper. How can you use this information to find the area of each rectangle?

_____

_____

6. Add up the areas you found in Step 5. Write your result below.

_____

7. Your result should be a reasonable estimate for the area of the circle. Use the formula *area* $= \pi r^2$ to calculate the area of the circle and evaluate your estimate.

_____

8. How could you modify the above method to get a better estimate of the area of the circle?

_____

_____

Granville T. Woods

Electrical Pioneer

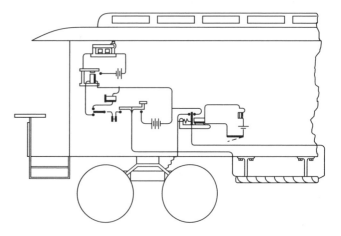

ranville T. Woods (1856–1910), an African-American inventor, engineer, and businessman, devoted his career to creating and improving electro-mechanical devices. His single most important achievement was the Railway Induction-Telegraph System, shown at the right. Woods developed relay equipment that allowed communication between a moving or resting train and the station. This device, often referred to as the "third rail," is still used in subway systems in New York City, Chicago, and other large cities.

Before Woods's invention, railroad stations could not communicate directly with moving trains. Stations telegraphed one another when a train left, and a system of signalmen passed the message down the line. This method was highly susceptible to human error and equipment failure. Unclear messages, poor weather conditions, bad wire connections, and distracted signalmen often resulted in serious train wrecks.

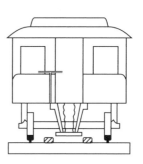

One of Woods's related inventions was called "Telegraphony." Telegraphony allowed people to speak through the same instruments that were used for sending telegraphs. This invention allowed an individual to transmit messages without a knowledge of Morse code. Woods also received patents for inventing or improving the following items: an electric incubator that could hatch 50,000 chicken eggs at one time, the Coney Island amusement park railway, an automatic circuit breaker, a phonograph, electromagnetic railway brakes, an electric light dimming system, and an electric railway conduit. Another important invention was the dynamotor, a device used to regulate electric motors. This device made electric motors safer by making it possible to use smaller resistance coils. (A resistance coil is similar to the coils you see inside a toaster.)

Granville Woods was born on April 23, 1856, in Columbus, Ohio. Because the Northwest Ordinance of 1787 prohibited slavery in the entire territory of which Ohio was a part, Woods was indeed free. He was able to attend school until he was ten years old, at which time he took a job in a machine shop. At sixteen, Woods went to Missouri and worked on railroads, first as a fireman and later as an engineer. During this time, he also experimented with electricity. When he was twenty years old, Woods moved to Springfield, Illinois, where he worked in a steel mill seven days a week and attended classes in the evenings. Although he finished his course of study, Woods's later career depended primarily on his lifelong self-education.

Granville T. Woods

Electrical Pioneer *(continued)*

A combination of hard work and genius allowed Granville Woods to produce one important invention after another. Some of his prominent clients were General Electric, American Bell Telephone, American Engineering Co., Universal Electric, and Westinghouse. Woods's successes, however, did not go unchallenged. He had to wage numerous costly court battles in order to defend his patent rights to certain inventions. Two notable battles were fought against Thomas Alva Edison. In each case, Woods was victorious. Edison later offered Woods a job in his company, but Woods declined the offer.

Granville Woods died on January 30, 1910, after suffering a stroke. Despite his many successes as a creative engineer and as a savvy businessman, Woods died in poverty. Henry E. Baker, assistant examiner in the United States Patent Office at the time, had this to say of Granville Woods: "... in his passing away he has left us the rich legacy of a life successfully devoted to the cause of progress." In 1974, Ohio Governor John J. Gilligan issued a proclamation in recognition of this great man who had more than 60 patents to his credit.

Questions for Critical Thinking

1. Why is it important for moving trains to be able to communicate with the station?

_____

_____

_____

2. Why might large resistance coils be unsafe in an electric motor?

_____

_____

_____

3. Granville Woods did not have formal training as an electrical engineer. What background did he have that made it possible for him to create his inventions? Give specific examples.

_____

_____

_____

_____

Granville T. Woods

Electricity at Rest

Materials: pencil, long balloon, stop watch or watch with second hand, wool fabric (optional)

Granville Woods's inventions involved the use of electricity. To create these inventions, he had to have a good understanding of its properties. Think about the types of electricity you experience in your everyday life. One example is the static electricity that you may observe when you take certain clothes out of a dryer. Another example is the electricity you use when you turn on a light. How are these forms of electricity similar? How are they different?

In this activity you will collect and analyze data relating to the properties of static electricity. The word *static* means "at rest." One way of thinking about static electricity is to think of it as electricity at rest.

Collecting Your Data

1. Inflate your balloon. "Charge" the balloon by rubbing it against your hair or on a piece of wool fabric. Once the balloon is charged, touch it to the wall or a low ceiling. After you remove your hand from the balloon it should remain on the wall or ceiling. Measure the length of time that the balloon stays up and record your result below.

_____

Analyzing Your Data

2. Using the table below, collect the data from each member of your class. Record it in the left column. Make sure the measurements you record all use the same unit of measure. For example, convert minutes to seconds if necessary.

Class Data	Ordered Class Data

3. In the right column, arrange the class data in order from the shortest time to the longest time. If any numbers occur more than once, list every occurrence. How many numbers do you have on your list? (This number is your sample size.)

_____

Multiculturalism in Mathematics, Science, and Technology

Granville T. Woods

Electricity at Rest (continued)

4. What is the longest time that any balloon stayed up? Describe anything different about this balloon.

_____

_____

5. What is the shortest time that any balloon stayed up? Describe anything different about this balloon.

_____

_____

6. Compute the *mean* for your data as follows. First, add all of the numbers on your list. Then divide this total by the sample size. Show your work and record the mean below.

_____

_____

_____

7. Compute the *median* for your data as follows. If the sample size is an odd number, find the number that is in the exact middle of your ordered list. For example, the median of {2, 6, 7} is 6. If the sample size is an even number, find the *two* numbers that are in the middle of the ordered list. Then add these numbers together and divide by two to find their average. For example, the median of {1, 6, 8, 12} is 7, since 7 is the average of 6 and 8. Show your work and record the median for your data below.

_____

_____

_____

8. Based on your analysis of the data, what conclusions can you make about the properties of static electricity?

_____

_____

_____

Granville T. Woods

Electricity at Work

Materials: pencil, two pieces of metal of different types (a penny and a nickel, wire scraps, etc.), one piece of fruit (or a small amount of any fruit juice, salt water, or vinegar), voltmeter

Granville Woods used the type of electricity that lights your home at night. This type of electricity can be thought of as "electricity at work." To provide electrical power for his inventions, Woods used many types of generators and batteries. The device you know as a battery is made up of units called *electrochemical cells*. Electrochemical cells use chemical reactions to produce a small amount of electricity.

In this activity, you will make an electrochemical cell based on the chemical reactions between metal and fruit juice. You will measure and record the amount of voltage produced and analyze similar data collected by other members of your class.

Electricity from Fruit

Place the two metals into the fruit, fruit juice, or other appropriate solution, so that the two metals do not touch. If you are using a solution, it is best to put the solution in a wide-mouth glass jar. In order to prevent the two metals from touching each other, you may have to tape each to the glass container. Some possible arrangements are shown in the illustrations below. Although your cell will produce some electricity, it will not be enough to light even a small flashlight bulb.

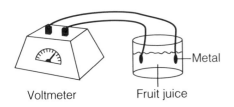

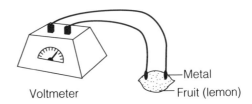

1. Connect each of your two metals to the voltmeter as shown above. Does anything happen? If so, what? Record your reading.

_____

_____

2. Draw your electrochemical cell in the space at the right. Label the items you used to construct it.

Multiculturalism in Mathematics, Science, and Technology

Granville T. Woods

Electricity at Work (continued)

3. Using the table below, collect the data from each member of your class. Record it in the left column. What unit of measurement are you and your classmates using?

Class Data	Ordered Class Data

4. In the right column, arrange the class data in order from the smallest to the largest voltage. If any numbers occur more than once, list every occurrence. How many numbers do you have on your list? (This number is your sample size.)

5. What was the largest voltage recorded? Describe anything different about this cell.

6. What was the smallest voltage recorded? Describe anything different about this cell.

7. Compute the mean and median for your data.

8. Based on your analysis of the data, what conclusions can you make about voltage and fruit-based electrochemical cells?

The Zuni

Ecology Technology

I n the international scientific community, there is a developing respect for American-Indian techniques of land and resource management. This respect is due to a growing awareness that these techniques are ecologically advantageous. Thousands of years before the arrival and influence of Europeans, the Zuni Indian tribe of present-day western New Mexico developed unique technologies to maintain the ecological well-being of their lands. The illustration at the right shows how a Zuni settlement looked when the first Europeans arrived in the 1500's.

Recently, the Zuni people have made great strides toward restoring and maintaining the environmental balance of their lands. The governor of the tribe, Robert Lewis, received the highest award in the United States for constructive ecological action. Zuni tribal member James Enote now leads a team of Indian and non-Indian scientists in a long-term model project. The project's goal is to restore and maintain the natural resources of Zuni lands. Incorporated into this plan is a return to an irrigation technology that the Zuni people had engineered long before the arrival of Europeans. This technique efficiently irrigates their fields and at the same time prevents erosion—a difficult feat in the arid environment of the southwestern United States.

The following quote from James Enote explains the Zuni technique.

In an area where rainfall is scarce and artificial irrigation is essentially nonfunctional, the Zuni Indians, for time immemorial, have used the power of experience and idea to design a system of irrigation that makes efficient use of limited rains, which occur as short but intense events. By carefully choosing locations within floodplains or intermittent stream channels, small diversions are built to capture and spread the infrequent runoff to irrigate fields. In this manner, crops are irrigated without expensive pipelines or ditches and erosion is reduced by slowing the flow of water across the land. Today, the expense of artificial irrigation in an arid environment is becoming more obvious and plans to increase the utilization of the traditional Zuni method of flood irrigation are being considered throughout the world.... By accomplishing this goal, the Zuni people will find themselves the object of international scrutiny when it becomes clear that time-proven ideas and an intimate understanding of nature's processes are easily the best approach to conserving the world's natural resources.

The Zuni

Ecology Technology (continued)

In the old days— and, actually, today still—Zuni farmers practicing floodplain irrigation used whatever materials were economically available. Depending on the location, materials consisted of rock, branches, shrubs, or logs. In any case, with limited resources, and usually without mechanized equipment, the idea of building a structure to divert water across the land is the same. No two structures are ever really constructed the same, so creativity and experience play a big part in the design. Essentially, *water must not undercut or wash out the structure* or it will damage crops and will have to be replaced.

In my experience, I have used cottonwood poles spaced about three feet apart and interwoven with willow branches. The idea is that grass, shrubs, and silt will eventually be caught in this net to create an impervious structure.

Another important feature is the angle of the structure within a channel or floodplain. If it is perpendicular to the channel, it will absorb too much energy and may fail. Ideally, the structures should spread water by diverting water smoothly from structure to structure in a zigzag pattern. In a model, twigs can mimic branches, grass can mimic shrubs, pebbles can mimic boulders, and so on, until the structure "feels" sensible and sturdy.

The Zuni irrigation and erosion-prevention structures described by James Enote are shown below. You will investigate how these structures can be placed for optimal erosion control in *Engineering Against Erosion*, the activity for this unit.

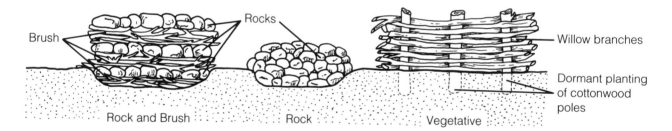

Questions for Critical Thinking

1. Describe erosion in your own words. Why is it advantageous to prevent erosion?

_____

_____

_____

_____

_____

The Zuni

Questions for Critical Thinking *(continued)*

2. Why do you think artificial irrigation is difficult in an arid, or dry, environment?

_____

_____

_____

_____

3. Throughout the years, what processes might the Zuni people have used to develop their special design for irrigation and erosion control?

_____

_____

_____

_____

4. In the Zuni design, why is the location of the "dams" important?

_____

_____

_____

_____

5. How might the Zuni design for irrigation and erosion control be used internationally?

_____

_____

_____

_____

_____

The Zuni

Engineering Against Erosion

Materials: pencil, clay dirt, two 1-gallon plastic jugs, 4 cardboard box "bottoms" (the type that hold 4 beverage six packs and measure approximately 25.5 cm by 35.5 cm by 6.5 cm), large heavy-duty trash bag, wide tape, sheet of heavy cardboard about 35.5 cm long and at least 10 cm wide, two boards at least 1 meter long

In order for people to grow enough food to survive, arid lands around the world have been irrigated and turned into farms. How can you irrigate arid lands without causing erosion? In this activity, you will design your own irrigation and erosion-prevention system. You will also build and analyze a model of the Zuni system.

First, assemble your model "field" according to the instructions and illustration below. When complete, it will resemble a makeshift "stream table" like those used in geology laboratories.

1. Pull down one of the long sides on two of the box bottoms. Pull down both long sides on the other two box bottoms. Fit all four box bottoms together to make one long box and tape the structure together. This will become your stream table. Line this long box with a trash bag that has been split open. The box should now be waterproof. Tape down the trash bag to the outside of the box so that it is secure.

2. Using one or more support boards, set up your stream table so that the top end is about 20 cm higher than the bottom end. Cut a V-shaped spout in the bottom end of the cardboard; do not cut the plastic trash bag. Press the plastic down into the spout so that water can flow out.

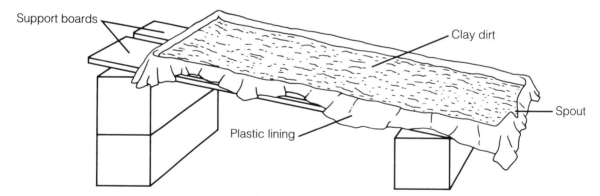

Support boards · Clay dirt · Plastic lining · Spout

3. Fill your stream table with clay dirt to within one centimeter of the top edge.

4. Cut one edge of your spare piece of cardboard to the shape shown in the figure at the right. Run the cut end of the cardboard down the dirt in your stream table so that it shapes the dirt to look like a shallow gully or valley.

approx. 35.5 cm

The Zuni

Engineering Against Erosion *(continued)*

5. Gently punch a pencil into the lower edge of one of the plastic jugs. Leave the pencil there as a plug. Set this jug at the top of the stream table. Cut off the top of the other plastic jug and position it so that it can receive water from the bottom spout of the stream table.

6. Fill the jug at the top of the stream table with one gallon of water. Unplug the pencil and let the water flow out at the top end of the "valley." Let it flow all the way down into the jug at the bottom.

7. What does this sudden one-gallon flow of water simulate?

_____

_____

_____

8. Repeat Step 6 twice. Record and describe your observations about the water flow, the water path, erosion, and materials going into the jug at the bottom of the stream table.

_____

_____

_____

9. Devise a plan to prevent the water from flowing so hard and fast down the valley. Design your system so that the water does not erode the valley and, at the same time, may be used to irrigate crops. Use only natural materials from around your school. Build and test your plan using several flows of water.

Describe your observations, being sure to address the following questions. Do you observe any erosion taking place? Where is the silt going? How has the rate and path of the water changed? How large an area is receiving water for crop irrigation?

_____

_____

_____

The Zuni

Engineering Against Erosion *(continued)*

10. Study the figure at the right. It shows how the Zuni people have engineered a solution to this situation. Their structures are called *aldiwe* (ahlth DEE way), which means "closure" in the Zuni language.

    Disassemble your model and reassemble a Zuni model. Test it several times and describe your observations.

    _____

    _____

    _____

    _____

11. How does the Zuni model compare to your original design?

    _____

    _____

    _____

12. Discuss why the Zuni *aldiwe* is being considered as a model for international projects.

    _____

    _____

    _____

An Extension

Redesign this activity into a formal, scientific experiment to compare the efficiency of different irrigation/dam designs. Use controlled variables and quantify your results. For example, to keep the amount of clay consistent, weigh the amount you put into the box each time. Use a measured amount of water each time and measure the runoff. Measure the flow rate of the water by placing a small floating object in the water and timing it. Keep data records so that you may compare the efficiency of the Zuni design to others. Analyze and determine the most efficient system.

Teaching Notes

The following teaching notes are designed to make it easy for the teacher to use the units. Notes for each unit include information on appropriate uses, prerequisites, and any necessary preparation. Whenever possible, suggestions are also provided for cooperative-learning groups and extension projects.

Maria Agnesi   Pages 9–12

Using the Unit

The activities on the curve of Agnesi are suitable for graphing lessons in Algebra I and Algebra II classes.

Prerequisites: Students should be comfortable working with quadratics and solving for one variable.

Additional Background

The curve known as the "witch of Agnesi" is more generally called a *versed sine curve*. Maria Agnesi did not "discover" the curve bearing her name. However, she wrote about its properties in the section of her book dealing with analytic geometry.

Bell-shaped curves, such as the curve of Agnesi, are among the most interesting and useful in mathematics. They occur in statistics as the *normal curve*.

The curve of Agnesi is an excellent lead-in or extension topic for a discussion of symmetry. For any value of the constant a in the equation $x^2y = a^2(a - y)$, the curve is always symmetric about the y-axis. This is reflected in the fact that x can be replaced by $-x$ in the equation of the curve without changing the equation.

The curve of Agnesi also ties in nicely with the concept of similarity. Varying the constant a results in a series of similar curves.

Extension Ideas

Have students research other "exotic" curves and their equations.

Al-Khowarizmi   Pages 13–16

Using the Unit

This unit is best used in an algebra class when discussing methods of solving quadratic equations.

The geometric models of al-Khowarizmi are an excellent introduction to solving quadratics by completing the square. The use of manipulatives (either algebra tiles or rectangles cut from paper) helps make the algebraic concepts more tangible for some students.

After students have completed the activity, you may wish to have them discuss their results and compare the two methods of solving quadratics. Ask them to describe advantages and disadvantages of each method.

Preparation

If algebra tiles are not available, you may wish to have students cut suitable squares and rectangles from paper before beginning the activity.

Additional Background

The Arabic name for the word *algebra* is a reminder that much of school mathematics had its beginnings in Africa, Asia, and the Middle East.

Al-Khowarizmi's book introduced Hindu numerals with their place-value system and zero symbol. The Islamic adoption of these numerals was an important contribution to Islamic civilization as well as later European civilization.

The Aztec   Pages 17–20

Using the Unit

Use this unit when studying area. The activity *Aztec Land Records* requires students to first estimate areas by counting graph-paper squares. Students should be encouraged to use estimation to evaluate the reasonableness of areas they find by calculation methods.

Prerequisites: Students need to know how to find the areas of rectangles and triangles.

Extension Ideas

Volume calculations can be made in connection with Aztec pyramids. Since Aztec pyramids are step pyramids, students can readily extend the strategy they used in the area problems. In the same way that quadrilaterals were divided into triangles and rectangles, step pyramids can be considered a series of parallelepipeds. The problem could be considered from the point of view of an Aztec engineer calculating the amount of stone and crushed rock needed to fill the core of a pyramid.

The Babylonians   Pages 21–24

Using the Unit

This unit can be included in discussions of the Pythagorean Theorem in algebra or geometry classes. *The Babylonian Right Triangle Theorem* activity is useful for introducing students to less-common Pythagorean triples. It also provides an opportunity for students to experiment with fairly large numbers on their calculators.

The activity *Estimating Square Roots by the Babylonian Method* would be appropriate in a pre-algebra course during lessons on square roots. You may wish to have students discuss strategies for choosing an initial guess.

Additional Background

The Pythagorean triples found on the tablet Plimpton 322 are especially impressive because the Babylonians did their calculations without modern tools. It is possible that this list of numbers was part of a pure mathematical investigation and had no immediate practical application.

The fact that an angle inscribed in a semicircle is a right angle was also known to the Babylonians.

Cooperative Learning

The Babylonian Right Triangle Theorem activity lends itself well to cooperative learning groups of three students each. One student can be responsible for using the calculator, another can be responsible for recording results in the table, and a third can be the group's spokesperson. Students in each group should agree on their final description of the relationship in the table.

Benjamin Banneker   Pages 25–30

Using the Unit

This unit can be used in science classes during discussions on mapping the earth, latitude and longitude, or astronomy. The unit is also appropriate for mathematics classes studying proportions.

As part of an introduction to any natural science, the *Capital Plan* activity on relative error and percent error would be useful for developing student skills in interpreting data. Pre-algebra teachers will find this activity useful when reviewing decimals and percents.

Prerequisites: It is helpful for students to have had some experience with proportions before using the activity *Moonrise in Your City*.

Additional Background

Benjamin Banneker is one of the most important personalities in African-American history. His life story is an inspiring example of an older person starting a new career in science. His story relates to topics in social science, mathematics, and earth science.

Although Banneker had a late start in astronomy, the 1790's were a very good time for scientific almanacs. The "problem of longitude" had recently been solved by the invention of the chronometer. This device kept accurate time aboard ships. Earlier failures to know exact longitudes caused the death of thousands of British sailors in the English channel. Columbus thought he had reached India because he underestimated the number of miles per degree longitude by 25%.

Cooperative Learning

The activity *Moonrise in Your City* lends itself to cooperative-learning groups. Students can work together to calculate moonrise times in different cities at 40° latitude. As an extension, cities at 40° latitude on different continents can be considered.

Celestino Beltran   Pages 31–34

Using the Unit

This unit may be used as part of an introduction to representing information graphically (for example, in pre-algebra). It is also suitable for use with discussions of computers and/or software.

Extension Ideas

You may wish to have students work together to prepare graphs of related data. For example, a group could choose to research weather data. Individuals in the the group might prepare graphs of monthly rainfall, average high temperature, average low temperature, wind speed, or other weather-related data. After the graphs are prepared, have the students discuss possible connections between their data. Have them present their conclusions and supporting data to the class.

Another option is to have students experiment with variations on bar graphs and line graphs. Possibilities include the use of icons or three-dimensional objects instead of grid squares in the bar graph.

A third option is to have students use a computer to explore graphing software. With graphing software, students can easily explore the use of different types of graphs to represent the same data. Many computer graphing programs are capable of extending graphs into the third dimension along a z-axis.

G. W. Carver   Pages 35–40

Using the Unit

This unit can be used as part of a lesson on soil, a lesson on materials cycling, or a lesson on carbon chemistry. Students should be well trained in laboratory safety precautions and procedures before attempting the activity *A Soapy Success Story*.

Preparation

It is recommended that you try the soap-making activity *A Soapy Success Story* ahead of time to become familiar with the process and identify any possible problems. Prepared peanut oil can be obtained in grocery or health-food stores in most areas. Sodium hydroxide (NaOH) and denatured alcohol can be obtained from scientific supply houses. You may want to stock the 40% NaOH solution and other reagents in laboratory squirt bottles to minimize the chance of pouring accidents.

For the activity *Plant Doctor, Soil Doctor*, you may want to have the students identify other soil-enriching materials ahead of time. A visit to a garden shop or nursery will provide them with many possibilities. Reference books for gardeners may also be helpful.

Cooperative Learning

Students should do the activity *A Soapy Success Story* with a laboratory partner. The day before the activity, have the partners meet and write up a laboratory plan detailing the procedures and each person's duties.

Extension Ideas

As an extension to *Plant Doctor, Soil Doctor*, have students research the process of composting. Have them develop a presentation or poster describing the chemical changes in a compost pile.

The Celts   Pages 41–44

Using the Unit

This unit may be used as part of a lesson on food chemistry in a life-science, physical-science, chemistry, or biology course.

Prerequisites: Students should be familiar with the idea that foodstuffs are composed of carbohydrates, fats, and proteins.

Preparation

Milk used for butter production must be full, non-homogenized milk with no additives. The cream must rise to the top and then be skimmed off. If possible, allow students to do this so they understand the entire process. If you decide to start with cream instead of milk, use full-fat (40% fat), non-homogenized cream with no additives. It is best to use a pasteurized product if possible.

To prepare soured cream, leave cream in a warm place (approximately 25° C) for at least 24 hours. Sources for these dairy products might be a grocery store, a local dairy company, a health-food store, or a local dairy farmer. You might even arrange for students to visit a dairy farm and milk the cows or observe them being milked.

The test plates for performing the nitric-acid test can be the type with depressions that are used in chemistry labs. Improvised petri dishes or test tubes can also be used.

It may take from 3 to 15 minutes of shaking to convert cream to butter.

Extension Ideas

Have students investigate using some form of electric power to help them make butter. Have them brainstorm possible techniques and then make butter using at least one of their techniques. When finished, students can compare the techniques and results with the more traditional methods used earlier.

Chu Shih-Chieh

Pages 45–48

Using The Unit

Binomial expansion is a topic from Algebra I. However, Pascal's Triangle can be introduced much earlier. Combinations and permutations can be discussed at almost any level of mathematics.

Protein Combo Plate may be used in science classes when discussing nutrition. It is also suitable for all mathematics classes when studying combinations.

Prerequisites: For *Pascal's Triangle and Binomial Expansion*, students should be able to multiply binomials.

Additional Background

Pascal's Triangle contains an almost unlimited number of interesting patterns. For example, the Fibonacci sequence (1, 1, 2, 3, 5, 8, 13, 21, 34, …) can be found by adding numbers on the diagonals of Pascal's Triangle. (The diagonals are parallel to a line through the second "1" on one side of Pascal's Triangle and the third "1" on the other side of Pascal's Triangle.)

Extension Ideas

Combinations occur throughout mathematics. An interesting study in combinatorics can be initiated with the discussion of the triangle congruence postulates in geometry. A triangle has six parts (three sides and three angles), yet, in many cases, congruence can be proved with a knowledge of just three congruent parts. Have students create a table of all possible combinations and determine which ones guarantee congruence.

Jewel Plummer Cobb

Pages 49–52

Using the Unit

This unit could become part of a lesson on the skin or a discussion of cell function.

Prerequisites: Students should be familiar with the basic concept of cell division and the parts of a cell.

Additional Background

Most of the cells of the basal layer of the epidermis are *keratinocytes*. These cells produce the fibrous protein *keratin*. They divide constantly, and the keratin-filled cells migrate upward to form the tough, protective covering of the skin surface. About 25% of the cells in the basal layer of the epidermis are melanocytes. Melanocytes can be thought of as one-celled "glands" that produce the pigment melanin. They have long, thin branches that extend between, and touch, the surrounding keratinocytes.

The pigment melanin is first produced in the cytoplasm of melanocytes. It is packaged in organelles called melanosomes that also contain the enzyme tyrosinase, which synthesizes melanin from the amino acid tyrosine. The melanosomes then travel out to the cell branches. Keratinocytes that are in contact with the melanin-laden cell branches take up the pigment by the process of *phagocytosis*. After the melanin enters the keratinocytes it tends to concentrate around the cell nucleus, particularly on the side exposed to sunlight. The location of the melanin suggests that it may function to protect the contents of the cell nucleus from damage by ultraviolet rays. Experimental evidence (like that in the activity *A Melanoma Experiment*) supports this hypothesis.

Extension Ideas

Have students do library research and write a report comparing melanoma to other forms of skin cancer.

Charles Drew   Pages 53–56

Using The Unit

This unit can be included in any lesson on the human circulatory system or any lesson on blood and the immune system. The content links advances in the understanding of the characteristics of blood types to the development of a life-saving institution (the blood bank).

Prerequisites: A basic knowledge of the composition of blood and its function in the body will help students understand the content.

Additional Background

A person's blood type is an important component of their biochemical identity. People with blood type A have a protein called A antigen on the surface of their red blood cells. Those with type-B blood have the B antigen. Type-AB blood occurs in people who have both A and B antigens on the surface of their red blood cells. People with type-O blood have neither type of antigen.

Problems with blood transfusions occur because of the response of the recipient's immune system to these antigens. Those with blood type A cannot receive transfusions of type-B blood because their antibodies recognize the type-B antigen as foreign. In this case, antibodies bind to the foreign blood cells and cause them to clump together and precipitate out of the blood stream. This creates a life-threatening crisis, as major blood vessels become blocked and body organs become clogged. Those with type-B blood cannot receive type-A blood for the same reason.

For those with type-AB blood, however, it is a different story. They accept the presence of both antigens and so can receive any type of blood. For this reason, those with type-AB blood are known as universal recipients. Those with type-O blood have no antigens on their blood cells and are known as universal donors.

Ancient Egypt I   Pages 57–60

Using the Unit

This unit is appropriate for geometry classes studying ratios, proportions, and scale drawings. The *Egyptian Coordinates* activity is also suitable for pre-algebra and algebra students studying the coordinate plane.

Prerequisites: Students should have some experience working with the coordinate plane.

Cooperative Learning

You may wish to have students work in pairs for the *Ideal Figure* activity. They can take turns using a tape measure to record the height of their partner's body parts. This tends to result in more accurate measurements. Students can also work together in setting up and solving the necessary proportions.

Additional Background

Students can gain insight into the importance of coordinates when they realize that coordinates were first used for a very practical purpose.

After the use described in the unit, the next known use of coordinates (also in ancient Egypt) was for another practical purpose. Rectangular coordinates were used in Egyptian star clocks, which told the hour of the night by the position of the brightest stars.

Ancient Egypt II   Pages 61–64

Using the Unit

A good time to introduce Egyptian multiplication is at the beginning of the year in algebra or any other time the distributive property of multiplication is discussed. A comparison with the modern multiplication algorithm gives students insight that they have been using the distributive property since elementary school.

The Very Large and The Very Small is appropriate for students who are exploring their scientific calculators. Some of the results may be surprising to students. Biology teachers may want to use this material in connection with bacterial population increase. Physics and chemistry teachers can discuss applications to radioactive decay and exponential growth.

Additional Background

Encourage students to study the method of Egyptian multiplication to discover why it works. They will find that the method depends on the distributive property. Using the example from the *Egyptian Multiplication* activity, $11 \times 33 = (1 + 2 + 8) \times 33 = 1 \times 33 + 2 \times 33 + 8 \times 33 = 33 + 66 + 264 = 363$.

It is interesting to note that the modern method of multiplication was introduced to Europe by Arabic-speaking Africans. The modern method probably had its origin in India.

Ancient Egypt III   Pages 65–68

Using the Unit

The Method of False Position may be used in algebra classes when discussing the solution of linear equations.

False Position and Second-Degree Equations may be used when introducing solutions to quadratic equations.

Prerequisites: Students should have some experience in working with proportions.

Additional Background

An advantage of the false-position method is that it encourages students to use trial and error in a guided, systematic way. You may wish to have students keep a list of their trial solution values and their outcomes.

Taking the square root of the correction factor when using false position with quadratics helps students understand degree in terms of dimension.

Extension Ideas

Have the class discuss various methods of solving equations. Ask them to describe advantages and disadvantages of each method.

Eratosthenes   Pages 69–72

Using the Unit

The unit on Eratosthenes is suitable for both mathematics and science classes. Mathematics teachers can use the unit with lessons on proportions, particularly as they relate to circles. Earth science teachers will find the unit useful during discussions of the earth's dimensions.

The *Circumference of the Earth* activity provides a natural opportunity for students to convert units of measure. Encourage students to use a proportion to convert stadia to meters.

Prerequisites: Students should be familiar with proportions and basic facts about parallel lines (for example, alternate interior angles are congruent).

Additional Background

Indirect measurement is the basis for many applications in mathematics and science. Trigonometry was first developed as a means of making indirect measurements. Many fields, such as astronomy and surveying, rely heavily on the principle of indirect measurement

Extension Ideas

Have students discuss possible sources of inaccuracy in Eratosthenes's calculation. For example, the distance between Syene and Alexandria would have been difficult to measure accurately in Eratosthenes's day.

Much of the work of Eratosthenes is suitable for student research projects. For example, you may wish to have students investigate the prime numbers. They can report on what is currently known and unknown about these numbers. The well-known "duplication of the cube" problem is another topic that should be accessible to most geometry students.

Bernardo Houssay   Pages 73–76

Using the Unit

This unit can be used as part of a discussion of the endocrine system or food chemistry.

Additional Background

Human insulin is a protein hormone made up of two polypeptide chains. One has 30 amino acids, the other 21 amino acids. The polypeptide chains are connected in two places by sulfur atoms, a type of connection known as a *disulfide bridge*. Frederick Sanger's research team at Cambridge University determined the amino-acid sequence of insulin in the early 1950's. The techniques they developed have been automated and can now be used to sequence much larger proteins. The amino-acid sequence of a protein is known as its *primary structure*. Because of the chemical properties of the amino acids, a polypeptide chain will fold and twist into a distinct three-dimensional structure. The unique three-dimensional structure of a protein hormone or enzyme determines its active properties.

Preparation

You may want to augment the food lists that the students use to design their menu plans. School dietitians may have nutritional information on school lunches and other foods. Many food packages contain analyses of carbohydrate, fat, and protein content. Students can be asked to collect this information before starting the activity.

The caloric recommendations in the unit are for growing adolescents. Generally, students over age 16 should use the lower calorie figure for their calculations.

Extension Ideas

Have students research the structure of insulin and make models of this protein hormone.

Hypatia   Pages 77–80

Using the Unit

Triangular, Square, and Polygonal Numbers is a problem-solving activity that can be used in pre-algebra, algebra, and geometry courses.

A Problem with Many Solutions can be used during a discussion of solutions to equations in an algebra class or after the Pythagorean Theorem has been introduced. Remind students that when they complete the table they should *not* complete rows for which $4n + 1$ is not prime. One such row, for $n = 2$, has already been filled in with X's.

Algebra II teachers may wish to introduce Hypatia when discussing the conic sections.

Cooperative Learning

The *Triangular, Square, and Polygonal Numbers* activity works well with cooperative-learning groups because students enjoy sharing their discoveries of patterns.

A cooperative-learning approach also works well in *A Problem with Many Solutions*. Students can combine their efforts to write numbers as the sum of squares.

Extension Ideas

Have students research additional applications of the conic sections.

As an extension of indeterminant equations, have students make up situations that lead to indeterminant equations. You may wish to have students provide one or more sample solutions to their problems.

The Incas   Pages 81–84

Using the Unit

This unit would be appropriate as part of a math or science lesson on graphical displays of data.

Additional Background

About 400 quipus have been found, mostly from excavations in desert regions. Most of what is known about quipus came from studies of these quipus and from two remarkable documents. One was written by a Spanish soldier, Pedro Cieza de León, who traveled throughout the Andes region in 1547. His account devotes a chapter to quipus and tells of their use in censuses, inventories, tax records, and in recalling songs and ballads. The other document, written about 65 years later, was an illustrated 1,179-page letter to the Spanish king from native-Andean Felipe Guamán Poma de Ayala. He outlined and illustrated the uses of quipus in running the precolonial government. The illustration of the Inca community official using a quipu is modeled after the one drawn by Guamán Poma de Ayala.

Cooperative Learning

A group of students can work together on the *Making a Quipu* activity. As a group, they can design and create a complex system of quipus containing related information. Each student can create one quipu to be attached to the others. Each quipu should be attached in a way that indicates its relationship to the others.

Harvey Itano   Pages 85–88

Using the Unit

This unit can be included in any lesson on human genetics. It is also appropriate in a biology lesson on the structure and function of proteins. The content links a change in molecular structure to its health effects on individuals.

Additional Background

Sickle-cell anemia is now among the best understood of human genetic diseases. It was only in 1905 that the disease began to be investigated in the United States. The first case described in U.S. medical literature tells of a young African-American man seen by a Chicago physician. The young man complained of pains in his joints and abdomen, chronic fatigue, and shortness of breath. Blood tests showed that his red blood cell count was very low, and that many of the cells were crescent-shaped (sickled), instead of the normal biconcave disk shape.

It was later discovered that sickled red bloods cells tend to stick together, forming clumps that block small blood vessels. This blockage frequently occurs in the joints and abdomen and causes severe pain. Sickled red blood cells are also very fragile and easily broken. This leads to a shortage of red blood cells (anemia).

Cooperative Learning

The activity *Deadly Disease or Life-Saving Trait?* can be done in small groups of two or three students. The students can work together to identify and compare the countries affected by malaria and sickle-cell anemia. They can then "brainstorm" ideas as to why these conditions occur together. Students should discuss their ideas and arrive at a group explanation for Question 4.

Ernest Just   Pages 89–94

Using the Unit

This unit may be used as part of a lesson on cell structure and function. It is also suitable for use with a discussion of reproduction, growth, and development.

Additional Background

A prominent member of Ernest Just's research team was an African-American woman, Roger Arliner Young. Dr. Just, known for his painstaking laboratory technique, thought that her work surpassed his own in "technical excellence." Young worked with Dr. Just at Woods Hole in the summers of 1927 and 1928 and also at Howard University. She played a major role in his research on such topics as the role of the cell membrane in fertilization, the role of electrolytes in hydration and dehydration in living cells, and the effects of ultraviolet radiation on the eggs of marine organisms such as the worm *Neresis*. On her own, she did research on the excretory apparatus in *Paramecia* that received international attention.

Preparation

If possible, use unwaxed cucumbers for the activity *The Cell Membrane—Master Regulator*. Wait until just before the activity to cut the cucumber, or have students slice their own.

Extension Ideas

Have students watch the cell membrane in action by observing living cells from the alga *Elodea* under the microscope. Students can prepare wet-mount slides of small fragments of *Elodea* fronds and then make drawings of the cell shapes they observe in solutions of plain water and 6% salt.

Omar Khayyam   Pages 95–98

Using the Unit

This lesson may be used in geometry classes after a discussion of Euclid's fifth postulate. It is ideal for classes studying non-Euclidean geometry.

Prerequisites: Students will need to use the Pythagorean Theorem and should be familiar with basic quadrilateral theorems.

Additional Background

A *non-Euclidean geometry* is one in which Euclid's fifth postulate is not satisfied. It is often useful to introduce non-Euclidean geometry in "standard" geometry classes so that students better appreciate the implications of Euclid's basic postulates.

Strictly speaking, the Pythagorean Theorem is easily extended to three dimensions. In this sense, the earth is a Euclidean space. However, the surface of a sphere, considered as a two-dimensional space, makes a good model of a non-Euclidean geometry. If straight lines on this surface are defined to be the great circles of the sphere, then there are no parallel lines. Students can discover for themselves that the Pythagorean Theorem does not hold on the surface of a sphere.

Omar Khayyam also advanced the study of cubic equations. He solved such equations by graphing a system of two conic sections and finding the coordinates of their intersection.

Cooperative Learning

This activity is well-suited to groups of two to four students. One student can be responsible for drawing the required figures, another can be responsible for taking measurements, and a third can be the group's recorder and/or spokesperson.

Sonya Kovalevsky   Pages 99–102

Using the Unit

A Look at Symmetry may be used in any mathematics class studying symmetry.

Infinite Sequences is suitable for pre-Algebra, Algebra I, or Algebra II classes studying patterns and sequences.

Additional Background

Patterns and sequences are among the most important strands in mathematics. Encourage students to find patterns in geometry, art, music, and other fields.

Some of the patterns in the *Infinite Sequences* activity may already be familiar to students. Sequence 2 is the triangular-number sequence (see page 79). Sequence 1, formed by successive doublings, is explored more fully on page 64 in *The Very Large and The Very Small*.

Extension Ideas

A Look at Symmetry can be extended by considering other types of symmetry, such as rotational symmetry and translational symmetry. Have students investigate the capital letters of the alphabet (as shown on page 101) for rotational symmetry. They will find that H, I, N, O, S, X, and Z have rotational symmetry.

Lewis Latimer
Pages 103–106

Using the Unit

This unit can be part of a lesson on electric circuits or a lesson on practical applications of electricity. Transformation of energy is an important idea in this unit, as Latimer's light converted electrical energy into light and heat.

Prerequisites: A basic idea of the nature of electric current is helpful for students in understanding their results.

Preparation

All materials for this activity are available at hardware and variety stores. As many of these are household items, you can also ask students to bring some of the materials from home. You may want to first try the activity yourself to be sure that everything works smoothly.

Additional Background

Incandescent light bulbs give off light and heat because the filament is highly resistant to the flow of electricity. Other household appliances rely on this principle. Any appliance designed to heat up (such as a hot plate, toaster, iron, heating pad, or electric space heater) depends on electrical resistance.

Cooperative Learning

Students should do the activity *Electric Experiences* in groups of two or three. Give students an opportunity to do hands-on work by having them take turns constructing the apparatus for the various parts of the activity.

Extension Ideas

Have students research the symbols used in circuit diagrams. They can then make circuit diagrams for each of the devices they build.

Jan Matzeliger
Pages 107–110

Using the Unit

The activity *Shoe Preferences and Data Analysis* provides an introduction to scatterplots and curve fitting. Although these topics are often covered in advanced courses, the activity is simple enough to be used in any class discussing the interpretation of data.

Prerequisites: Students should be familiar with the coordinate plane.

Cooperative Learning

The activity *Shoe Preferences and Data Analysis* is designed for students working in pairs. During Step 1 of the activity, remind students to fill in the "Your Ranking" column independently. Only after both students have completed this step should they reveal their rankings.

Extension Ideas

Have students survey two of their friends or family members about other preferences, such as food, movies, or sports. Have students prepare and interpret scatterplots to analyze the level of agreement between those surveyed.

The Maya   Pages 111–114

Using the Unit

Addition with Maya Numerals may be used in any mathematics class when discussing place value. Although this activity can be done with only paper and pencil, the use of manipulatives is strongly recommended. The use of beans or popcorn kernels for the dots and toothpicks for the bars greatly simplifies addition.

The *Maya Time Cycles* activity uses the concept of the least common multiple of two numbers. For earth science or physical science students, this activity provides deeper insight into our own calendar and the idea of periodicity.

Additional Background

The Maya lived in the Yucatan, Guatemala, and parts of El Salvador and Honduras. The three main periods of the Maya civilization were Pre-classic (ca. 1500 B.C. to 300 A.D.), Classic (300 to 900), and Postclassic (900 to 1697).

Extension Ideas

Maya multiplication is a good research project. Although there is no evidence that the Maya used multiplication, it is not difficult to perform multiplications with manipulatives. A few simple rules are needed. The dot is the identity element and the usual rules apply. For example, dot × dot = dot, dot × bar = bar. Also, bar × bar = bar, with one dot carried one place above the place of the multiplier or multiplicand, whichever is higher.

Ynez Mexia   Pages 115–118

Using the Unit

This unit could become part of a discussion of ecology or a lesson on the plant kingdom.

Students in biology classes may already be familiar with the use of taxonomic keys. You may want to locate reference books for them to use in identifying their plants.

Remind students not to pick, crush, or otherwise damage the plants. They should also take care to minimize plant damage when they set up the grid with their stakes and string.

If a camera is available, have students take photos of their study areas for later reference.

Prerequisites: Students should have been introduced to the factors determining plant growth or basic plant physiology.

Preparation

You may need to locate a suitable area where students can set up their grids. To get the most interesting results, try to chose an area with different microhabitats. If students choose their own sites, it is important to inspect the sites to be sure that students have not chosen a hazardous area. Possible hazards include toxic plants (such as poison oak or poison ivy) and unstable ground (such as that near cliffs or river banks). It may be necessary to obtain permission from private property owners.

Extension Ideas

Have students choose a second study area with slightly different environmental conditions. For example, the second area might get more sun or have different soil. Have students repeat the activity and compare the variety and distribution of plants.

Native Americans I   Pages 119–122

Using the Unit

This unit may be included in a lesson on ecology or in a lesson on earth cycles (such as the water cycle, the carbon-oxygen cycle, or the nitrogen cycle). The content is particularly useful in integrating ideas from the life, earth, and physical sciences in the thematic context of the circle as a universal pattern of nature.

Additional Background

Many cultures share the idea that nature is like a circle. For many thousands of years, this idea has figured prominently in the philosophical systems and literature of Asian civilizations. Indigenous peoples living close to nature in all parts of the world consider this to be the most obvious and fundamental of all ideas about nature.

In the 1970's, James Lovelock, a scientist from Great Britain, connected the modern science of ecology with the concept of the earth as a living "superorganism." He gave this superorganism the name of a mythical earth goddess, Gaia. According to Lovelock, life actually shapes the climate and atmosphere of planet Earth. There is much evidence for this idea. For example, water transpiration by tropical forests produces clouds that affect global weather patterns. The oxygen in the atmosphere is produced by living things and has remained at a more or less constant level (15% to 25%) for 200,000,000 years. Lovelock further maintains that life on earth acts in a coordinated way to keep the earth "livable." This aspect of Lovelock's theory, which has become known as the *Gaia hypothesis*, is more controversial.

Extension Ideas

Have students do fieldwork at a nearby natural environment to observe and identify relationships between organisms and the physical environment.

Native Americans II   Pages 123–126

Using the Unit

This unit may be included in any lesson on plants or genetics that features the concept of hybridization.

Preparation

The amount of water to be used in the activity *Growing Corn and Potatoes* may need to be modified to suit the environmental conditions and soil type in your area. You may want to experiment with this ahead of time.

Corn seeds are available from local nurseries. Potatoes can be obtained from a grocery store or nursery. A large range of Native-American seeds are available from Native Seeds/Search, 2509 North Campbell #325, Tucson, AZ, 85719. Catalogs are available for $1.

Additional Background

Native-American civilizations are located in a wide variety of environments. This is especially true of the Inca civilization that thrived in the Andes Mountains. The Incas developed corn and potato varieties for environments as diverse as high, cold, mountain terraces, low, warm valleys, and humid jungles. The many different varieties must have been developed by experimentation and the use of cross-breeding techniques.

Cooperative Learning

Groups may have as many as ten students, with each student responsible for one box. Rotating responsibilities can be established so that one student is not "stuck" with a slow-growing or non-growing box. Have the students hold regular group discussions of their results. Point out that these discussions parallel those that must have taken place among ancient Native-American agriculturalists and still take place among modern agricultural scientists.

The Navajo I   Pages 127–130

Using the Unit

Creating a Burntwater Design is appropriate in geometry classes during the study of transformations and symmetry.

Prerequisites: It is helpful if students are familiar with the concept of symmetry.

Extension Ideas

Have students research other Navajo rug patterns. Students should pay particular attention to the types of transformations and symmetry in the designs. *Navajo and Hopi Weaving Techniques* by Mary Pendelton (Macmillan, 1974) and *Indian Blankets and Their Makers* by George W. James (Dover, 1974) are good resources.

The Navajo II   Pages 131–134

Using the Unit

This unit can be used with a biology lesson on bacteria or a health lesson on antiseptics and antibiotics.

Prerequisites: Students should have a basic understanding of the growth of bacteria on a nutrient medium.

Preparation

Prepared sterile petri dishes filled with nutrient agar, wire inoculating loops, and pure cultures of *Staphylococcus aureus* are available from scientific supply houses.

The pitch must be obtained from a species of pine. You can obtain pine pitch during an outing to a pine forest, at a local nursery or Christmas tree yard, or by gently heating or steaming knots in a pine board.

Sterilize all bacterial cultures before disposal.

Additional Background

The bacteria in this activity, *Staphylococcus aureus*, are part of normal human skin flora. When the protective barrier of the skin is breached by a wound, the bacteria are introduced into a rich growth medium of blood and intercellular fluids. The bacteria then begin to grow in large numbers. The body responds with increased blood flow to the wound site and the proliferation of white blood cells to attack the invading bacteria. This is known as the inflammatory response and results in the symptoms of infection (redness, localized warmth, swelling, and pus).

Extension Ideas

Have students use similar methods to test other antiseptics.

Hideyo Noguchi
Pages 135–138

Using the Unit

This unit can be included in a lesson on bacteria or in a lesson on health and disease. You may wish to take the opportunity to discuss syphilis as a sexually transmitted disease and a major public health problem.

Additional Background

After declining for more than thirty years, the number of cases of syphilis reported in the United States is showing a drastic increase. The number of cases reported in 1990 was more than triple the number of cases reported the year before. It is estimated that 80% of all cases go unreported. These are frightening statistics, because syphilis, although treatable, is a very serious disease.

The first symptom of syphilis is a painless sore on the genitals which can go unnoticed. The sore heals in a few weeks. Several weeks later, a rash appears on the body. Fever and swollen lymph glands may also occur. These second-stage symptoms also disappear in a few weeks without treatment. If syphilis is not treated, several years may pass without further symptoms. The infected person is still capable of infecting others for about two years. During this time, the disease severely damages the body. Three to four years after infection, serious final symptoms occur. These include heart failure, blindness, paralysis, mental disorders, and sometimes death.

Early treatment can prevent the disease from progressing. Syphilis is usually treated with injections of an antibiotic (usually penicillin). However, syphilis, like other sexually transmitted diseases, is preventable.

Extension Ideas

Have students research other diseases studied by Noguchi. These include oroya fever, yellow fever, polio, and rabies.

Srinivasa Ramanujan
Pages 139–142

Using the Unit

This unit is well suited to geometry classes studying the area of circles. However, the concept of pi can be introduced in algebra classes during the discussion of irrational numbers.

In *A Geometric Method of Estimating Pi*, encourage students to be creative in counting the dots. For example, students may be able to count the dots in the quarter circle quickly by grouping them into large rectangles or by first counting the dots in $\triangle ABC$.

Prerequisites: To complete the activity *A Geometric Method of Estimating Pi*, students should be familiar with the formula for the area of circle.

Cooperative Learning Groups

A Geometric Method of Estimating Pi lends itself to cooperative-learning groups. Students can brainstorm ideas for counting the dots efficiently.

Extension Ideas

Have students prepare a short report on one of the topics that Ramanujan wrote about. Topics might include pi, infinite series, number theory, and infinity.

Eloy Rodriguez   Pages 143–146

Using the Unit

This unit could become part of lessons on plants, carbon chemistry, or even the nature of the scientific method. The activity is designed to provide students with a problem-solving situation. Students should try to figure out which extraction method and chromatography solvent will best separate the chemical constituents of their particular herb. This may require more than one attempt on their part and could become an ongoing activity.

Preparation

You may want to experiment with the herbs ahead of time, and develop a clear chromatogram to use as an example. Encourage students to bring appropriate herbs or spices from home. Remind them to use *whole* herbs, rather than crushed or powdered forms. For example, if they bring cinnamon, it should be in the form of bark.

The materials list describes equipment and supplies available from science supply companies as well as the materials' homemade equivalents. A modified glass medicine dropper can be made as follows: heat the dropper in a flame until the glass begins to soften and melt; using another piece of glass, draw out the end so that it forms a very fine tip.

Additional Background

The active chemical constituents of herbs are contained in their essential oils. If these oils are very volatile, the plants will have a strong fragrance, like that of mint. If a tea is made from herbs of this type, simmering or steeping in a covered vessel will prevent the volatile oils from escaping into the air. Herbs that feel oily or sticky to the touch are good candidates for solvent extraction.

The Sami   Pages 147–150

Using the Unit

This unit could become part of a physical-science or physics lesson on forces and motion.

The idea of friction as a force opposing motion can be introduced with this activity. Before beginning, discuss these concepts with the class. A review of the difference between weight and mass is also appropriate.

A review of laboratory safety rules may be in order. Discuss the safe use of sharp instruments and hot steam before beginning.

Prerequisites: Students need to be familiar with the concept of forces and should understand the newton (the SI unit of measure for forces).

Preparation

It is recommended that you try this activity first. As you work through the activity, the force of friction (and the coefficient μ) should lessen as the skis are modified.

A 2.5-newton spring scale is best for measuring the forces in this activity. You may have to adjust the weight of the load to optimize students' results. Balsa wood in standard sheets of $\frac{3}{32}$" by 3" by 3" can be found in most hobby shops and is relatively inexpensive.

Have water simmering in a wide, stable, heat-proof container to serve as a steam source. Allow only a few students at the steam source at one time.

Extension Ideas

Have students conduct an analysis of modern skis in real snow. They can apply the general techniques of this activity and use a heavy-gauge spring scale to measure the forces involved.

Seki Kowa Pages 151–154

Using the Unit

Although matrices are not explicitly used, the activity *Determinants and Systems of Equations* is recommended for Algebra II classes working with matrices and systems of equations. However, the activity can be used in Algebra I classes as an alternative to the graphing, substitution, and addition methods of solving systems of equations.

Prerequisites: Students should have experience in solving two equations in two unknowns.

The Yenri Method is suitable for geometry classes studying the area of circles. This activity gives students a preview of some of the methods used in calculus.

Cooperative Learning Groups

You may wish to have groups of students work through *Determinants and Systems of Equations*. Then have them solve a variety of systems using all of the methods they have learned. Students can discuss the advantages and disadvantages of each method.

Extension Ideas

The determinant method of solving systems of equations makes a useful and challenging computer programming project. Have students begin with two equations in two unknowns. Algebra II students can then proceed to three equations in three unknowns and four equations in four unknowns. Encourage students to integrate the programs for two, three, and four equations into one computer algorithm for the cleanest possible program. You may need to remind students to consider cases in which the determinant is 0.

Granville Woods Pages 155–160

Using the Unit

This unit may be used as part of a discussion of static electricity or electrochemical cells.

The activity *Electricity at Rest* is suitable for mathematics classes studying the mean and median. The activity provides an easily-accessible connection between mathematics and science.

Additional Background

In 1884, Granville T. Woods and his brother Lyates Woods founded the Woods Electric Company in Cincinnati, Ohio. The company manufactured equipment for the telephone, telegraph, and electrical industries. At the time, this was one of the few companies owned and operated by African Americans.

Preparation

Try to choose a dry day for the activity *Electricity at Rest*. Any moisture in the air will affect the outcome.

A variety of fruits, juices, and other solutions can be used to make the electrochemical cells in *Electricity at Work*. Have students bring items from home for this activity. If your school does not have a small voltmeter, you can purchase one from an electronics store.

Cooperative Learning

In *Electricity at Rest*, you may wish to have students compile data from their group, rather than the entire class. Afterward, the groups can come together and compare results. This presents a good opportunity to discuss the importance of sample size in obtaining statistically meaningful results.

The Zuni   Pages 161–166

Using The Unit

This unit may be used as part of a geology or ecology lesson on erosion or water flow. Students need only some initial familiarity with the implications, effects, and processes of erosion. Before beginning, you may want have a class discussion about erosion to assess the students' level of prior knowledge.

The style of the *Engineering Against Erosion* activity is trial-and-error or informal experimentation. For this reason, it is important to let students experiment with their model field or stream table before they see the Zuni "solution." It is useful to withhold the last page of the activity (page 166) containing the diagram of the Zuni *aldiwe* until students have completed Step 9.

Additional Background

Students can better understand the climatic conditions in the Zuni area by locating the region on a world map or globe. If students trace a line across the map or globe at the latitude of the Zuni area, they will notice that many of the places at this latitude (North Africa, the Middle East, etc.) are also arid. Rainfall at this latitude is minimal due to patterns of global air circulation driven by the heating and rising of air at the equator.

Cooperative Learning

The activity *Engineering Against Erosion* is best done in cooperative-learning groups. Students will need to work as a team to properly operate and observe the stream table. Be sure that students take turns at the various tasks, such as shaping the stream bed, pouring the water, and observing and recording data.

Answers

Answers are provided for all questions in the units. In many cases, answers to open-ended, critical-thinking questions are simply suggestions for possible student responses. Such questions can provide an ideal opportunity for class discussion.

Maria Agnesi   Pages 9–12

Questions for Critical Thinking

1. Being multilingual allows you to communicate directly with people from different countries and different backgrounds. This is especially important in exchanging scientific ideas.   **2.** In the 18th century, women were not allowed many of the opportunities afforded to men.   **3.** Cartesian plane, Pascal's Triangle, Venn diagram, etc.   **4.** Answers may vary.

The Curve of Agnesi

1. $x^2y = 4(2 - y)$ **2.** $y = 8/(x^2 + 4)$ **3.** $(-3, \frac{8}{13})$, $(-2, 1)$, $(-1, \frac{8}{5})$, $(0, 2)$, $(1, \frac{8}{5})$, $(2, 1)$, $(3, \frac{8}{13})$
4. It is a bell-shaped curve, symmetric about the y-axis.   **5.** For $a = 5$, the equation is $x^2y = 25(5 - y)$. This produces a similar curve, with y-intercept $(0, 5)$.

The Curve of Agnesi: Another Approach

6. The curve is bell-shaped, symmetric about the y-axis, with y-intercept $(0, 1)$.   **7.** $a = 1$

Al-Khowarizmi   Pages 13–16

Questions for Critical Thinking

1. Alkali, alfalfa, etc.   **2.** Descartes (cartesian plane), Pasteur (pasteurize), etc.   **3.** Negative solutions have many practical applications. For example, they can be interpreted as temperatures below zero.   **4.** Land-area calculations, tax calculations, etc.   **5.** Hindu-Arabic numerals produce more compact numbers and are easier to work with when doing arithmetic.

A Geometric Model for Solving Quadratic Equations

Completing the Square   **1.** 16   **2.** $x^2 + 8x + 16 = 33 + 16$ **3.** $(x + 4)^2 = 49$ **4.** $x + 4 = 7$, $x + 4 = -7$ **5.** $x = 3, -11$ **6.** 3 ft
Al-Khowarizmi's Geometric Model   **4.** 4, 16   **5.** 49   **6.** 7   **7.** $7 - 2 - 2 = 3$ ft

The Aztec   Pages 17–20

Questions for Critical Thinking

1. As a minimum, arithmetic operations would have been needed to calculate prices and change.   **2.** Answers may vary. Numerals for commerce may have been quicker to write and use.   **3.** Favored buyers would want a longer measuring stick. Favored sellers would want a shorter measuring stick.   **4.** Pyramids can collapse unless carefully planned and accurately measured.

Aztec Land Records

(Estimates may vary. Actual areas are given.) **1.** 45   **2.** 24   **3.** 12   **4.** 56   **5.** 42   **6.** 150

The Babylonians   Pages 21–24

Questions for Critical Thinking

1. Good clay was plentiful in the area.   **2.** The large number of clay tablets that have been found show that there was enough surplus food to feed many scribes.   **3.** The theorem gives the distance between two points on the coordinate plane.   **4.** The number 60 is evenly divisible by many whole numbers.   **5.** Answers may vary.

The Babylonian Right Triangle Theorem

1. The numbers in the right column are larger than those in the middle column.
2. $120^2 + 119^2 = 169^2$ **3.** 120   **4.** The numbers in the left column are: 120, 3456, 4800, 72, 360, 2700, 960, 600, 6480, 60.   **5.** The sum of the squares of the numbers in the left and middle columns equals the square of the number in the right column.

Estimating Square Roots by the Babylonian Method

1. a. 4   **b.** $\frac{15}{4}$ **c.** 3.875   **d.** $3.875^2 = 15.016$ **2.** 3.8729833   **3.** It is slightly larger.
4. Different initial guesses will give different estimates.

Benjamin Banneker   Pages 25–30

Questions for Critical Thinking

1. Only seven planets were known in 1790 because of the limitations of the telescopes used then.   **2.** Mercury, Venus, Earth, Mars, Jupiter, Saturn, and Uranus   **3.** Possible answers include library research, direct observation, questioning peers, etc.   **4.** No, it would not work. It would be difficult to coordinate train and plane schedules, national broadcasts, and other large–scale events.   **5.** In the days before electric lighting, knowing the time of sunrise and moonrise was useful for travelers and farmers. People living in rural areas today still find this information useful, although most urban dwellers do not.   **6.** The property boundaries must be marked, roads and streets must be laid out in straight lines, etc. If surveying were not done before building the city, it would be a random jumble of buildings and it would be more difficult to get around. Also, it is likely that there would be many property disputes.   **7.** He needed to calculate and design his gears to maintain the fixed ratios of sixty seconds to one minute and sixty minutes to one hour.

The Capital Plan

1. Side *A*: error 230.6 ft, relative error 0.0044, percent error 0.44%; Side *B*: error 63 ft, relative error 0.0012, percent error 0.12%; Side *C*: error 263.1 ft, relative error 0.005, percent error 0.50%; Side *D*: error 70.5 ft, relative error 0.0013, percent error 0.13%   **2.** The percent error for each side is one-half of one percent or less. This is quite small.

Benjamin Banneker   *Continued*

Moonrise in Your City

4. See table below.   5. Latitude, longitude, time zone

City	Longitude (deg/min)	Longitude (decimal)	Longitude Divided by 360°	Longitude Time Correction	Local Time Correction	Moonrise 12/22/91
Philadelphia	75° 9′	75.15°	0.209	16 min.	1 min.	6:20 P.M.
Columbus	83°	83.00°	0.231	18 min.	32 min.	6:53 P.M.
Indianapolis	86° 10′	86.17°	0.239	19 min.	45 min.	7:07 P.M.
Denver	104° 59′	104.98°	0.292	23 min.	0 min.	6:26 P.M.
Sacramento	121° 30′	121.50°	0.338	26 min.	6 min.	6:35 P.M.

Celestino Beltran   Pages 31–34

Questions for Critical Thinking

1. Computers can only process information according to the instructions contained in a software program.   2. Answers may vary. Learning to use a computer makes it possible for anyone to find work and business opportunities.   3. Answers may vary. See the flow chart on page 31 for an example.

Graphs to Go

Answers to Questions 1 through 7 will vary depending upon the student's choice of data. 8. The graphs have similar axes and represent the same data.   9. The line graph connects data points; the bar graph does not.

George Washington Carver Pages 35–40

Questions for Critical Thinking

1. Peanuts, pecans, and sweet potatoes grow well in the South.   **2.** Plants have many different chemical constituents in their roots, leaves, and stems.   **3.** Different plants have different mineral requirements. If the same crop is planted year after year, it will completely extract certain minerals.   **4.** Climate and soil conditions might be similar.

A Soapy Success Story

9. The test tube with the soap will foam and the oil will no longer separate. The test tube without soap will still have distinct oil droplets that separate into an oil layer.   **10.** Soap seems to make oil "dissolve" in water so that it can be washed away.   **11.** Answers may vary. Students may comment on the color and aroma of commercial soaps.

Plant Doctor, Soil Doctor

1. Animal manure contains nitrogen, phosphorus, potassium, calcium, magnesium and sulfur.   **2.** Corn stalks contain carbon.   **3.** The following materials or combinations contain the three most important plant nutrients: hay, pine needles, leaves, animal manure, straw with bone meal, food scraps with bone meal and wood ashes, cottonseed meal with bone meal and wood ashes, blood meal with bone meal and wood ashes.   **4.** Students should describe supplementing the soil with materials containing phosphorus, potassium, and calcium. Some possibilities include: bone meal with wood ashes, hay with eggshells, pine needles with eggshells, and straw with bone meal.

The Celts Pages 41–44

Questions for Critical Thinking

1. Students may have prior knowledge of how butter is made from cream or they may recall information from the media about how butter is high in cholesterol and saturated fat. **2.** Answers may vary. Someone making whipped cream may have gone too far and formed butter, or perhaps cream was accidentally shaken too much while being transported.   **3.** The protein structures wrap around or enclose fat molecules in tiny globules. The sketch should reflect an outer protein covering with fat on the inside.   **4.** Water from the cream goes into the buttermilk. Butter has only 16% water, while buttermilk is mostly water (91%). Fat from the cream is liberated and goes into the butter, which is 80.6% fat, while buttermilk is only 0.4% fat. Protein coverings remain in the buttermilk liquid, which is 3.4% protein, while the butter is only 0.6% protein.

The Celts   *Continued*

The Chemistry of Butter

2. Soured cream (it turns into butter faster and with less effort)   **3.** Soured cream and buttermilk are acidic and will turn the blue litmus paper red. The other items are nearly neutral and should have little, if any, effect on either litmus paper.   **4.** The souring effect was acidic. A sour taste may be a sign of acid in foods.   **5.** In order of fattiness (most to least): butter, cream (sour or sweet), milk, buttermilk.   **6.** Buttermilk contains little or no fat because the fat formed butter and was removed.   **7.** In order of protein content (most to least): buttermilk/milk (about equal), soured cream/cream (about equal), butter (may show a trace or no reaction)   **8.** See Question 7.   **9.** Answers may vary. Protein is in milk and cream; when butter is made, the fat is removed and the protein remains in the buttermilk.

Chu Shih-Chieh   Pages 45–48

Questions for Critical Thinking

1. Answers may vary. It may be because the great works of Chu Shih-Chieh were lost for many years.   **2.** The next rows are 1, 7, 21, 35, 35, 21, 7, 1 and 1, 8, 28, 56, 70, 56, 28, 8, 1. **3.** The next two numbers are 21 and 28. The sequence is 1, 1 + 2, 1 + 2 + 3, ….   **4.** The triangular numbers occur in the third "diagonal row" of Pascal's Triangle.   **5.** Answers may vary. Students may notice the whole numbers in the second "diagonal row" of the triangle.

Pascal's Triangle and Binomial Expansion

1. $a^2 + 2ab + b^2$ **2.** The coefficients (1, 2, 1) occur in the third row.   **3.** $a^3 + 3a^2b + 3ab^2 + b^3$ **4.** The coefficients (1, 3, 3, 1) occur in the fourth row.   **5.** $a^4 + 4a^3b + 6a^2b^2 + 4ab^3 + b^4$ **6.** $a^8 + 8a^7b + 28a^6b^2 + 56a^5b^3 + 70a^4b^4 + 56a^3b^5 + 28a^2b^6 + 8ab^7 + b^8$ **7.** Use the $(n + 1)$th row.

Protein Combo Plate

1. Bottom row of table: 1, 2, 1   **2.** Possible combinations: none, rice only, beans only, corn only, rice and beans, corn and beans, corn and rice, rice and beans and corn. Bottom row of table: 1, 3, 3, 1. Nutritional needs are met by: rice and beans, corn and beans, rice and corn and beans.   **3.** The numbers occur as a row of Pascal's Triangle.   **4.** 6

Jewel Plummer Cobb   Pages 49–52

Questions for Critical Thinking

1. The cancerous cells are growing out of control and forming a tumor mass. The non-cancerous cells divided until they formed a single layer.   **2.** The mechanism for making melanin is the same in humans and animals because humans and animals are related. **3.** Exposure to sunlight stimulates the melanocytes to make more melanin, darkening the skin.   **4.** Color changes are possible because of shifting pigment within cells. When pigment disperses around the cell membrane, the cell appears darker. This process is different from tanning since it involves the movement, rather than the creation, of melanin.

Jewel Plummer Cobb   *Continued*

Analyzing Cell Growth

1. In the graph at the left, the cells stop growing when they reach a certain number. In the graph at the right, they continue to grow indefinitely.   2. The graph at the left shows the growth of normal cells because they stop dividing at some point.   3. The graph at the right shows the growth of cancerous cells because they continue to divide indefinitely.   4. Titles and labeling may vary, but should reflect the answers to Questions 2 and 3.

A Melanoma Experiment

1. The more-pigmented tissue slices survived X-ray treatment better than the less-pigmented tissue slices. The more-pigmented tissues withstood higher doses of X-rays.   2. Tissues with more melanin were resistant to X-rays, so the melanin seems to have a protective effect. The protective effect of melanin may be the reason that melanomas do not respond to standard radiation treatments.

Charles Richard Drew   Pages 53–56

Questions for Critical Thinking

1. Karl Landsteiner's work made it possible to type and match blood for compatible transfusions. Without this information, it would not have been possible to organize a working blood bank.   2. A blood bank is an important idea because it allows blood to be preserved and stored for emergency transfusions.   3. The doctor must be sure that the blood to be transfused does not carry any disease organisms such as the hepatitis virus or HIV. 4. Dr. Drew's work was important in his time because of the many seriously wounded soldiers and civilians needing transfusions during World War II.   5. Blood carries oxygen, nutrients, hormones, and other substances to all of the body's cells.   6. By making blood banks possible, Dr Drew's research has saved many lives all over the world.

Keeping Blood Fresh

1. Generally, when blood is kept cold it decomposes more slowly.   2. The best temperature seems to be 4° C. A colder temperature is too close to the freezing point of water, a major component of blood. When kept warmer than 4°C, blood decomposes more quickly. 3. Sodium citrate has a preservative effect and, at the right temperature, slows decomposition.   4. The best concentration of sodium citrate was approximately 5%. Blood stored with that concentration of sodium citrate took the longest time to separate.   5. The best conditions for preserving whole blood would seem to be at 4°C, with a 5% solution of sodium citrate added as a preservative. The worst would be at 25°C, with or without sodium citrate.

The Ancient Egyptians I   Pages 57–60

Questions for Critical Thinking

1. Answers may vary. There probably will not be 7 palms to the cubit.   **2.** $\frac{1}{28}$ **3.** It is unlikely that any pharaoh fit the ideal proportions.   **4.** Answers may vary. Careful planning and measurement certainly played a part in such accuracy.

The Ideal Figure

Answers will vary depending upon measurements taken by students. The rightmost column of the table should be filled in with the "ideal" number of squares for each body part given on page 57.

Egyptian Coordinates

1. The Egyptian coordinates (middle column of the table) are: 3 cubits, 3 palms, 2 fingers; 3 cubits, 2 palms, 3 fingers; 3 cubits; 2 cubits, 3 palms; 1 cubit, 3 palms, 1 finger; (no entry).
2. The vertical coordinates in fingers (right column of table) are: 98, 95, 84, 68, 41, 0.

The Ancient Egyptians II   Pages 61–64

Questions for Critical Thinking

You may wish to have students check each other's work for Questions 1 through 5.
6. Egyptian numerals have no zero symbol, Egyptian numerals usually result in longer expressions than modern numerals, Egyptian numerals were used to write numbers from right to left (although they would read the same in either order), etc.   **7.** These numbers occur on the body (fingers and toes).

Egyptian Multiplication

5. 33 + 66 + 264 = 363   **6.** 27 + 108 + 216 = 351   **7.** 672 (occurs in last row of table)

The Very Large and the Very Small

1. The numbers get smaller.   **2.** Most scientific calculators will give an error message after enough divisions by 2. Some may read 0.   **3.** No   **4.** The numbers get larger.
5. 1.2089×10^{24} **6.** d

The Ancient Egyptians III   Pages 65–68

Questions for Critical Thinking

1. It was developed to simplify practical problems.   **2.** Planning pyramids, calculating areas, etc.   **3.** Answers may vary. The method of false position has the advantages of working for any initial guess and requiring only basic arithmetic.   **4.** Answers may vary. The equations and solutions may have been recorded as a guide for future engineers.

The Ancient Egyptians III   *Continued*

The Method of False Position

1. $x + \frac{1}{3}x = 21$ **2.** 3 (Answers may vary.)   **3.** 4, no   **4.** $\frac{63}{4}$ **5.** This value checks in the original equation.   **6.** The initial choice of a trial value does not matter. However, some values are easier to work with than others.

False Position and Second-Degree Equations

1. $x^2, \frac{9}{16}x^2$ **2.** $x^2 + \frac{9}{16}x^2 = 100$ **3.** $4^2 = 16$, and this eliminates the fraction.   **4.** 25   **5.** 4
6. $2 \times 4 = 8$ **7.** 8 by 8 and 6 by 6

Eratosthenes   Pages 69–72

Questions for Critical Thinking

1. The distance to the sun, the depth of an ocean, the diameter of the solar system, etc.
2. Answers may vary. The areas around the Middle East and the Mediterranean Sea were mapped most accurately.   **3.** Answers may vary. The areas around southern Africa and the eastern part of Asia were mapped least accurately.   **4.** Australia, North and South America, Antarctica   **5.** Answers may vary. Regions near Eratosthenes's home were mapped most accurately. Other regions were as yet unknown in his part of the world.

The Circumference of the Earth

1. The three angles are congruent.   **2.** $m\angle 3 = 7.2°$ **3.** $7.2:360 = 5000:C$ and $C =$ 250,000 stadia   **4.** 250,000 stadia; 46,250,000 meters; 46,250 kilometers

The Length of Africa

2. 65°   **3.** $65:360 = x:40,000$ **4.** 7,222 km   **5.** The part of Africa with the longest length must be on the circumference of the circle.

Bernardo Houssay   Pages 73–76

Questions for Critical Thinking

1. Weakness, excessive thirst, and frequent urination   **2.** The pituitary gland produces hormones that control other glands in the endocrine system.   **3.** People with diabetes may respond better to human insulin than to insulin from another species. Synthetic insulin can be produced cheaply and in unlimited quantities.   **4.** When the blood glucose level rises after a meal, the pancreas produces insulin. The insulin stimulates the cells to take up the glucose, returning the blood glucose level to normal. If the blood glucose level falls below normal, the pancreas produces glucacon. The glucagon stimulates the liver to release glucose into the blood, returning the blood sugar level to normal. Glucagon is a hormone that acts to keep the blood sugar level from dropping too low, acting as a counterbalance to insulin.

Bernardo Houssay   *Continued*

What's on the Menu?

1. Students should calculate the approximate number of calories required by multiplying their body weight (in pounds) by the calories-per-pound guidelines described on page 75.
2. Students' proposed menu plans will vary. A sample menu for a moderately-active female student weighing 100 pounds (requiring 1900–2400 calories) is described below.

Breakfast: half-cup fruit juice, two slices toast with margarine, one egg, one cup lowfat milk (carbohydrates: 57 grams, protein: 28 grams, fat: 28 grams, calories: 605)
Lunch: Turkey and cheese sandwich with mayonnaise and lettuce, one orange, one cup lowfat milk (carbohydrates: 72 grams, protein: 35 grams, fat: 24 grams, calories: 655)
Dinner: 3 oz. roast beef, one baked potato with margarine, half-cup cooked green beans, tossed salad with Thousand Island dressing, sliced bananas, sparkling water (carbohydrates: 50 grams, protein: 26 grams, fat: 44 grams, calories: 705)
Snack: one apple (carbohydrates: 30 grams)

3. Answers may vary. Students may comment on the lack of high-sugar foods in the diabetic diet as compared to their own.

Hypatia   Pages 77–80

Questions for Critical Thinking

1. Answers may vary. Alexandria's location may have contributed to its rise as a center of learning. It was also a wealthy civilization.   **2.** Parabolic satellite dishes, elliptical orbit of the moon, circular wheels, etc.   **3.** Advances in astronomy (due to improved telescopes, etc.) made the conic sections relevant to scientists in the 17th century.   **4.** Such measurements would have been used for navigation.   **5.** Answers may vary. It is unlikely that many women followed in their father's profession at the time.

Triangular, Square, and Polygonal Numbers

1. 10, 15   **2.** 1, 4, 9, 16, 25   **3.** Triangular: 1, 3, 6, 10, 15, 21, 28, 36, 45; Square: 1, 4, 9, 16, 25, 36, 49, 64, 81; Pentagonal: 1, 5, 12, 22, 35, 51, 70, 92, 117; Hexagonal: 1, 6, 15, 28, 45, 66, 91, 120, 153; Heptagonal: 1, 7, 18, 34, 55, 81, 112, 148, 189   **4.** Answers may vary. The second column contains consecutive whole numbers, the numbers in the third column can be found by adding 3 to the number in the row above, etc.

A Problem with Many Solutions

Rows 4 through 9 of the table should be filled in as follows. 4, 17, 1 + 16, 289, 64 + 225; 5, 21 (not prime), X, X, X; 6, 25 (not prime), X, X, X; 7, 29, 4 + 25, 841, 400 + 441; 8, 33 (not prime), X, X, X; 9, 37, 1 + 36, 1369, 144 + 1225   **1.** All of the prime numbers in the second column (5, 13, 17, 29, 37) are solutions to the problem.   **2.** Student conjectures may vary, but all primes of the form $4n + 1$ *are* solutions to the problem.

The Incas   Pages 81–84

Questions for Critical Thinking

1. Answers may vary, but could include the scores of sporting events, debts, election data, etc.   **2.** Answers may vary. A possible arrangement might be two cords attached to a main cord. One cord could be used to record income, the other to record expenditures. A third cord, attached in between those two and oriented in the opposite direction could be used to keep a running tally of the difference between income and expenditures.   **3.** Answers may vary. Traffic signals use the color green to mean "go," red to mean "stop," and yellow to mean "prepare to stop."   **4.** Cotton and wool were widely available and easy to transport.

Making a Quipu

Situation 1: Data tables should be similar to those below.

Bag	Weight	Time	Temperature
1	W_1	1	T_1
2	W_2	2	T_2
3	W_3	3	T_3
		4	T_4

Possible quipu formats include a group of 3 cords separated by a space from a group of 4 cords, or a group of 3 cords in one color next to a group of 4 cords in a second color.

Situation 2: Data tables should be similar to those above. Quipu formats may vary. One possible arrangement is a main cord with two cords attached (one for each area). To each area cord, four cords are attached to represent each storehouse. To each storehouse cord, a brown, white, and red cord are attached to keep blanket tallies.

Harvey Itano   Pages 85–88

Questions for Critical Thinking

1. Symptoms of anemia include weakness, dizziness, headache, drowsiness, and general malaise.   **2.** Lack of iron in the diet, loss of blood, variations in hemoglobin structure, or any condition that reduces the number of red blood cells   **3.** The mutation causing sickle-cell anemia may have survived because it had positive, as well as negative, effects.

Patterns of Inheritance

1. 0%   **2.** 50%   **3.** 25%   **4.** 50%

Deadly Disease or Life-Saving Trait?

1. Countries affected by sickle-cell anemia include Zaire, Angola, Zambia, Zimbabwe, Ghana, Ivory Coast, parts of Algeria, Madagascar, Saudi Arabia, Yemen, Burma, Italy, Spain.
2. Countries affected by the malaria parasite include Zaire, Angola, Zambia, Zimbabwe, Ghana, Ivory Coast, Kenya, Somalia, Ethiopia, Sudan, parts of Algeria, Burma, Iran, Thailand, Indonesia, Philippines, Australia.   **3.** Zaire, Angola, Zimbabwe, Ghana, Ivory Coast   **4.** Answers may vary. The actual explanation is that people who are heterozygous for sickle-cell anemia have enhanced resistance to malaria.

Ernest Just   Pages 89–94

Questions for Critical Thinking

1. Dr. Just's observations suggested that there was something going on in the cytoplasm, and he decided to investigate further.   **2.** The proteins in the cell membrane control the movement of materials in and out of the cell.   **3.** The symptoms of many diseases might be caused by improperly functioning cells. Studying cell function would help determine how to get diseased cells working properly.   **4.** Bees and ants produce many individuals with genes from only one parent.   **5.** The larval and adult forms take advantage of different food resources and survival strategies. Many flying insects have wormlike larval forms.

Which Came First?—Embryology of the Sea Urchin

1. The sequence is as follows: single-egg cell, single-egg cell surrounded by the fertilization membrane, two-celled stage, four-celled stage, multi-celled ball, hollow ball (blastula), flattened hollow ball (early gastrula), "pocketed" ball (late gastrula), pre-larva (larva-shaped gastrula), larva.   **2.** Students should describe the process outlined above in Question 1.

The Cell Membrane—Master Regulator

1. The cell at the right (the water is exerting pressure against the cell walls, causing them to bow out)   **3.** Color, texture, smell, firmness, etc., should be noted.   **4.** In general, the mass of the salt-treated slice should decrease slightly and the mass of the water-treated slice should remain the same or increase slightly.   **5.** Students may comment on how the salt-treated slice has shriveled or shrunk.   **6.** Students may comment on how the water-treated slice has softened or become waterlogged.   **7.** The salt treatment caused water to come out of the cells by the process of osmosis. The salt concentration was higher outside the cells than inside the cells, so the water moved out. In the water-treated cells, the salt concentration was higher inside the cells than outside the cells, so water moved in.

Omar Khayyam   Pages 95–98

Questions for Critical Thinking

1. Mathematics was used for practical purposes in other sciences.   **2.** Similar: both study the positions of planets; Different: astrology includes the belief that the planets can influence the affairs of people.   **3.** Sample postulate: given two points, there is exactly one line containing them.   **4.** Answers may vary. Students may note that Khayyam was not a modest man.

A Look at Euclid's Fifth Postulate

1. 5 in.   **2.** They are congruent; rectangle   **4.** No   **5.** No; no   **6.** No   **7.** The postulate does not hold on the surface of a sphere (i.e., in "curved space").

Sonya Kovalevsky
Pages 99–102

Questions for Critical Thinking

1. She faced discrimination in many areas because she was a woman. **2.** "Existence" means there is a solution. "Uniqueness" means there is only one. **3.** They were first sighted in 1610 by Galileo, they are made up of tiny particles, etc. **4.** Answers may vary. Students may note that both research mathematics and fiction writing require imagination.

A Look at Symmetry

1. You may wish to have students check each other's drawings. **2.** Vertical: A, H, I, M, O, T, U, V, W, X, Y; horizontal: B, C, D, E, H, I, K, O, X; both: H, I, O, X **3.** Circle, line, etc.

Infinite Sequences

1. 64, 128, 256 (powers of 2) **2.** 28, 36, 45 (1, 1 + 2, 1 + 2 + 3, …) **3.** 46, 53, 60 (arithmetic sequence) **4.** 19, 23, 29 (primes) **5.** 0, –1, 0 (oscillating) **6.** Seq. 3; 7 **7.** Seq. 1; 2

Lewis Howard Latimer
Pages 103–106

Questions for Critical Thinking

1. Thermal (when the filament gets hot, it gives off light) **2.** The filament becomes brittle from extreme heat. **3.** The bulb with the thicker filament would not produce as much light.

Electric Experiments

1. The filament **2.** Current flows through the foil, into the bulb, heats the filament, and produces light. **3.** This should make no difference. **4.** Each bulb is half as bright. **5.** Bubbles form around the foil leads. **6.** The nail becomes an electromagnet.

Jan Matzeliger
Pages 107–110

Questions for Critical Thinking

1. The shoe-lasting machine carried out more processes than the sewing machine. **2.** The invention put many people out of work. **3.** Shoes became less-expensive and more readily available. **4.** Advantages: shoes were interchangeable, probably easier to make, etc; disadvantages: did not fit as well, less comfortable, etc.

Shoe Preferences and Data Analysis

3. Answers may vary depending upon student responses. **5.** The line represents complete agreement between those surveyed. **6.** The line represents complete disagreement between those surveyed. **7.** Students should take into account their responses to Questions 5 and 6. For example, a scatterplot with points clustered around the line through (1, 1) and (10, 10) would indicate general agreement.

The Maya   Pages 111–114

Questions for Critical Thinking

1. Answers may vary. The number may have been chosen because people have 20 fingers and toes.   **2.** They were able to accurately measure solar and lunar cycles (upon which calendars are based).   **3.** Answers may vary. Possibilities include spring and autumn equinoxes, motions of planets, etc.   **4.** Possibilities include the solar cycle (1 year), the seven-day cycle (1 week), etc.

Addition With Maya Numerals

5. 258 is represented by 2 bars and 2 dots in the 20's row and 3 bars and 3 dots in the units row. 402 is represented by 1 dot in the 400's row, a zero symbol in the 20's row, and 2 dots in the units row. The sum is 660, which is represented by 1 dot in the 400's row, 2 bars and 3 dots in the 20's row, and a zero symbol in the units row.

Maya Time Cycles

1. 6   **2.** 12   **3.** Find the least common multiple of m and n.   **4.** 18,980   **5.** 52

Ynez Mexia   Pages 115–118

Questions for Critical Thinking

1. *Biological diversity* means the variety of species of plants, animals, and other organisms living on Earth.   **2.** Such photographs might tell scientists what other plants and animals are found near the plant, the plant's preferred growing conditions, etc.   **3.** The Amazon has better year-round growth conditions.   **4.** Common names can help scientists identify plants with potential medicinal properties.

A Plant Diversity Survey

2. Items such as slope, soil type, available water, and sun vs. shade, should be included.
6. Factors affecting plant growth include water, sunlight, temperature, grazing pressure, and competition from other plants.   **7.** Students should look for relationships between their diversity data and the physical environment. For example, "Few types of plants grew here because there was little sunlight."

The Native Americans I   Pages 119–122

Questions for Critical Thinking

1. Round raindrops, the curve of a rainbow, whirlpools, etc.   **2.** Many answers are valid. Examples of humans not acting as part of nature include pollution, habitat destruction, over-population, etc. Examples of beneficial influences include land reclamation, work with endangered species, etc.   **3.** Students can use this question to explore values. Answers may vary.

The Native Americans I   *Continued*

Circles, Cycles, and Ecosystems

1. Trees, grasses, shrubs, deer, wolves, insects, birds, etc.   **2.** Trees provide nesting sites for birds, insects eat trees and flowers and provide food for birds, etc.   **3.** Plants need light provided by the sun, animals need water from the rain, etc.   **4.** Algae, minnows, frogs, water birds, etc.   **5.** Algae provide food for minnows, insects eat microorganisms, frogs and birds eat insects, etc.   **6.** Plants and animals need sunlight and water from the physical environment.   **7.** The use of dead trees as nesting sites, the role of fallen leaves in enriching the soil, etc.   **8.** New plants and animals would starve. The forest or pond could not continue.

The Native Americans II   Pages 123–126

Questions for Critical Thinking

1. You may wish to have students check each other's calculations.   **2.** Livestock feed, corn starch, paper products, etc.   **3.** They have provided basic nutrition, a greater variety of food, etc.   **4.** Evidence is provided by the diversity of corn and potato varieties adapted for many environments.   **5.** Answers may vary. One possibility is that Europeans took these plants back to Europe and did not acknowledge Native Americans.

Growing Corn and Potatoes

8. Varieties that grow well in the desert could be sent to northern Chile, where there is a large desert. There are many other possibilities.

The Navajo I   Pages 127–130

Questions for Critical Thinking

1. These colors occur naturally in wool.   **2.** Each rug is considered a unique work of art. **3.** Symmetry, reflections, coordinates, etc.   **4.** Answers may vary.   **5.** Answers may vary. However, symmetry may make the rugs easier to weave since patterns are repeated and/or reversed.

Creating a Burntwater Design

1. Answers will vary depending upon students' designs. Most will have at least a vertical and horizontal line of symmetry.   **2.** 21; add the two previous numbers to get the next. **3.** Use a rotation as well as a translation in the border design, orient the *hokha* differently, etc.

The Navajo II   Pages 131–134

Questions for Critical Thinking

1. Answers may include hydrogen peroxide, iodine, etc. These help stop bacterial growth.
2. It helps prevent the growth of infection-causing bacteria.   **3.** Pine trees have an antibacterial chemical in their pitch as an adaptation for survival. Cedar trees may have a different survival strategy.   **4.** Some possibilities include aspirin, codeine, quinine, aloe vera, etc.   **5. and 6.** Answers may vary. These questions are suitable for class discussion.

Pine Pitch Antiseptic

7. Students may predict that bacteria in the dish with pine pitch will be affected in some way.
9. In the dish with no pine pitch, bacteria will grow up to the edge of the filter paper. In the dish with pine pitch, there will be a visible zone of inhibition where bacteria cannot grow.
10. Yes. Bacteria did not grow in or near the area where pine pitch was applied.

Hideyo Noguchi   Pages 135–138

Questions for Critical Thinking

1. Spirilla   **2.** The bacteria might have attacked the brain and spinal cord so that messages from the brain could not get to the muscles.

Bacterial Growth

1. The number of bacteria are 1, 2, 4, 8, 16, 32, 64, 128, 256.   **2.** The graph should be upward sloping.   **3.** 262,144   **4.** The number of bacteria will continue to increase more and more rapidly.   **5.** No. Growth will slow down when the nutrient supply is exhausted.   **6.** 2^n

Srinivasa Ramanujan   Pages 139–142

Questions for Critical Thinking

1. He had to overcome poverty and language barriers.   **2.** Hardy was formally trained in mathematics, Ramanujan was not; Ramanujan came from a background of poverty, Hardy did not.   **3.** Answers may vary.   **4.** Pi is irrational. Formulas are needed to get decimal (rational) approximations for use in applications.   **5.** Possible advantage: the ability to go at one's own speed; possible disadvantage: "standard" topics may be missed.

Circles and Pi

2. $C \div D$ should always be about 3.14.   **3.** $C \div D$ is constant.   **4.** Yes; π is approximately 3.14.

A Geometric Method of Estimating Pi

2. $\frac{1}{4}\pi r^2$ **3.** r^2 **4.** $\frac{1}{4}\pi$ **5.** About 1960; 2500   **6.** Answers will vary, but should be close to 0.785.   **7.** Multiply by 4. This should give a result close to 3.14.

Eloy Rodriguez   Pages 143–146

Questions for Critical Thinking

1. Vitamin C or tea for colds, salt-water gargles for sore throats, etc.   **2.** This was probably discovered through trial and error, and possibly by watching animals.   **3.** An argument in favor might be that herb remedies are more gentle. An argument against might be that they contain a mixture of chemicals, some of which could have unknown effects.   **4.** Perhaps they feel it is important to make new discoveries, or they like nature, or they enjoy uncovering the pharmaceutical effectiveness of remedies from their heritage.   **5.** Without expert advice, poisonous or inappropriate plant materials might be ingested.

Analyzing Herbs

5. Students should describe such things as whether the herb is dried or fresh, any detectable aroma, texture, etc.   **9.** Answers may vary, but should contain something to the effect that an herb contains many chemical constituents.

The Sami   Pages 147–150

Questions for Critical Thinking

1. It was important for mobility, hunting, and herding. Skis are important to the rest of the world for snow and sports uses.   **2.** Sleds, skates, snow glasses, use of snow as a water source, etc.   **3.** Ski shape is important for maneuverability and speed. The fastest shape is long and thin. The slowest is short and broad.   **4.** Changes include the number of poles used, overall length, and turned-up ends.   **5.** These changes were made to reduce friction and prevent skis from digging into the snow.

Ski-Design Testing

5. Generally, the crude ski will sink somewhat and dig into the snow.   **6.** The more the ski sinks, the greater the force required to move it.   **8., 9.,** and **10.** Values of μ should decrease.

Seki Kowa   Pages 151–154

Questions for Critical Thinking

1. Answers may vary.   **2.** Seki may have been afraid of someone else taking credit for his discoveries.   **3.** He probably drew a diagram, assigned variables, and used geometric properties and algebra.   **4.** The area of a rectangle is easy to calculate.

Determinants and Systems of Equations

1. $-9; -11$ **2.** $x = -3, y = 2; x = 7, y = 2$ **3.** The method works as long as the determinant is not 0. (If the determinant is 0, the equations are either inconsistent or multiples of each other.)

Seki Kowa   *Continued*

The *Yenri* Method

5. The area of each rectangle is its width times its height. Since the width is 1, the height gives the area.   **6.** Answers should be somewhat smaller than the actual area of the circle, about 314 cm^2.   **7.** 314 cm^2; estimates should be smaller than this.   **8.** Use narrower rectangles.

Granville T. Woods   Pages 155–160

Questions for Critical Thinking

1. Moving trains must notify the station of their location and speed to avoid collisions.
2. Large resistance coils might heat up and cause a fire.   **3.** Woods's work experience as a railroad engineer and firefighter may have helped him invent the railway induction telegraph, railway brakes, and other related inventions.

Electricity at Rest

Answers for Questions 1 through 7 will vary depending upon class data.   **8.** Answers may vary, but should mention the fact that static electricity exerts a force that can work against gravity to hold a charged object against a ceiling or wall.

Electricity at Work

Answers for Questions 1 through 8 will vary depending upon class data.

The Zuni   Pages 161–166

Questions for Critical Thinking

1. Answers should contain the idea that erosion is the carrying away of soil or other surface material by the action of water or wind. Advantages to preventing erosion include: preventing the loss of topsoil in which plants grow, preventing the silting up of waters downstream, etc.   **2.** Artificial irrigation is difficult in an arid environment because it is costly, water is easily lost to evaporation, etc.   **3.** The Zuni developed their techniques by many years of trial and error, as well as communication with one another about techniques and design developments.   **4.** They optimize the use of available water.   **5.** The design could be used internationally in other arid environments. It is a low-cost system suitable for many poor countries. It can easily be built by small communities.

Engineering Against Erosion

7. It simulates a rain shower.   **8.** Students will observe a fast-moving stream of water carrying a large amount of dirt with it.   **9.** Observations will vary. Generally, students will try to divert water flow around a series of obstacles.   **10.** The *aldiwe* model will slow the water flow. Irrigation area is maximized.   **11.** Generally, the Zuni model will perform better. …is an effective, low-cost solution to the problem of erosion caused by irrigation.